PRENTICE HALL MATHEMATICS

GEOMETRY

Informal Geometry

Lesson Plans and Assessments

PEARSON

Prentice Hall

Boston, Massachusetts
Upper Saddle River, New Jersey

ISBN: 0-13-165745-3

1 2 3 4 5 6 7 8 9 10   10 09 08 07 06

Informal Geometry Lesson Plans

● Contents

Introduction

To the Teacher of Informal Geometry Students

Geometry, more than any other area of mathematics, engenders strong feelings in students. Students' opinions about geometry, as well as their understandings, fit a wide range. Some students have yet to develop the problem solving, spatial visualization, and reasoning skills that are critical to success in a typical geometry course. Some students may have a minimal level of mathematics knowledge and experiences to bring to a geometry class. Still other students may struggle with a language or cultural barrier that has prevented them from succeeding in previous mathematics courses. An informal geometry course may be best for these students.

Research conducted by a Dutch couple in the mid-Twentieth Century helps us understand how students progress through levels of reasoning in geometry. Pierre and Dina Van Hiele were public school mathematics teachers when they gathered the data that lead to the development of these five levels:

Level 0: Visualization
Students recognize figures but do not recognize their properties.

Level 1: Analysis
Students analyze component parts of figures, but interrelationships between figures and properties can not be explained.

Level 2: Relationships
At this level, abstract relationships among figures are understood. Informal proofs can be followed. However, students do not see how the logical order of the proof can be altered.

Level 3: Deduction (High school geometry)
Reasoning at this level includes the study of geometry as a formal system. The interrelationship and role of undefined terms, definitions, theorems and formal proof is seen, which allows the development of a proof in more than one way.

Level 4: Rigor (College level geometry)
The study of geometry at this level is very abstract and with a high degree of rigor.

All students must progress through Visualization, Analysis, and Relationships in order to reach Level 3, Deduction. This is the level at which students can write proofs and is generally the required for success in a typical high school geometry course. However, many students enter geometry while still operating at lower Van Hiele levels. Thus, some activities in an informal geometry class must focus on visualization and description of geometry figures before focusing on analysis of the relationships between them. Also, it may not be reasonable to expect all informal geometry students to be able to write formal proofs. Students in an informal geometry course may instead be asked to outline proofs, examine existing proofs for errors, or supply missing steps for proofs. Paragraph proofs may be more meaningful than formal proofs for such students.

An informal geometry teacher may want to use various teaching approaches. Students in an informal geometry class need additional time to explore relationships using concrete materials. Class lectures accompanied by blackboard demonstrations should be used less frequently. De-emphasize drill on geometry facts and relationships, since mathematics learned by rote memorization may be quickly forgotten. To help students develop understanding of critical concepts, we recommend completely working through every one of the textbook's Investigations in class. These Investigations help illuminate various geometric relationships. The ancillary, *Geometry Hands-On Activities,* can also be used to develop concepts prior to a more formal presentation in the student text. Additionally, such students may benefit from working with peers in small groups, where they may be more willing to present findings or ask meaningful questions than they would in a large class setting. As the *Principles and Standards for School Mathematics* (NCTM, 2000) suggest, it is in the relative privacy of small groups where students will fully engage mathematics by talking about it with their peers.

The Student Edition chapters themselves have full-page features on Vocabulary Building, Guided Problem Solving, Activity Labs, and Test-Taking Strategies. Student Edition Answers are available on transparencies to facilitate homework review. The student edition appendices contain aids such as Skills Handbook, Illustrated Glossary, a list of Tables and Formulas, and a list of all Theorems and Properties.

There are many aids, provided by this program, designed specifically to help with your informal geometry class. The Teacher's Edition of Prentice Hall Geometry contains valuable information in the margins of every section that highlights what knowledge is necessary for students to succeed in that section. The Teacher's Edition margin notes include Alternate Methods, Error Prevention, and Math Background.

Transparencies show the Additional Examples from the Teacher's Edition margin, Daily Check Skills You'll Need (including worked out solutions), and lesson quizzes.

To ensure that you obtain your goal in meeting the needs of all students, especially those with special needs, other teaching resources are available. *Chapter Grab & Go Files* provide Reteaching and Practice worksheets for every lesson, as well as two Checkpoint Quizzes for each chapter.

To ensure that students of varied abilities will be successful in demonstrating competency in achieving the objectives of the Prentice Hall Geometry program, a variety of formal assessment measures is offered. These include chapter tests, cumulative tests for quarterly assessments, mid-course assessment, and end-of-course assessment.

The F form Chapter Test is equivalent to the D form Chapter Test found in the Geometry *Grab & Go Files*. The Quarter, Mid-Course, and Final tests are equivalent to the same tests found in the Geometry *Progress Monitoring Assessments*. Each test may have been modified to parallel the topics covered in the Informal Geometry lesson plans.

To allow time for visualization and description activities, some advanced topics might be omitted from the course. The Scope of Course, Pacing Guide, and the Lesson Plan pages of this Planning Guide indicate which topics are suggested for an informal geometry course.

The components include: Introduce, items that you can use as warm up; Facilitate, a description of the lesson's mathematical background; Objectives, New Vocabulary, NCTM Standards; and a specific exercise assignment guide. Additionally, Resource Options lists all the Teaching Resources, Transparencies, and Technology components that have been specifically designed to go with each lesson.

In today's world, All students must acquire proficiency in geometric thinking. The Prentice Hall Informal Geometry Lesson Plans and Assessments will assist you in giving your students the opportunity to gain this proficiency.

Leveled Pacing Guide

B = Below Level   O = On Level   A = Advanced

Chapter 1 Tools of Geometry	B	O	A
1-1 Patterns and Inductive Reasoning	✔	✔	✔
1-2 Drawings, Nets, and Other Models	✔	✔	✔
1-3 Points, Lines, and Planes	✔	✔	✔
1-4 Segments, Rays, Parallel Lines and Planes	✔	✔	✔
• Vocabulary Builder: Geometry Vocabulary	✔	✔	✔
1-5 Measuring Segments	✔	✔	✔
• Algebra 1 Review: Solving Linear Equations	✔	✔	
1-6 Measuring Angles	✔	✔	✔
1-7 Basic Constructions	✔	✔	✔
• Activity Lab: Compass Designs	✔	✔	✔
• Activity Lab: Exploring Constructions		✔	✔
1-8 The Coordinate Plane	✔	✔	✔
• Activity Lab: Distance in the Coordinate Plane	✔	✔	✔
• Guided Problem Solving: Understanding Word Problems	✔	✔	
1-9 Perimeter, Circumference, and Area	✔	✔	✔
• Activity Lab: Comparing Perimeters and Areas	✔	✔	✔
• Activity Lab: Linear Regression		✔	✔

Chapter 2 Reasoning and Proof	B	O	A
2-1 Conditional Statements	✔	✔	✔
2-2 Biconditionals and Definitions	✔	✔	✔
2-3 Deductive Reasoning	✔	✔	✔
• Activity Lab: Mathematical Systems		✔	✔
2-4 Reasoning in Algebra	✔	✔	✔
• Activity Lab: Paper-Folding Constructions	✔	✔	✔
• Guided Problem Solving: Understanding Math Problems	✔	✔	
2-5 Proving Angles Congruent	✔	✔	✔
• Activity Lab: Applying Reasoning		✔	✔

Leveled Pacing Guide (continued)

B = Below Level   **O = On Level**   **A = Advanced**

Chapter 3 Parallel and Perpendicular Lines	B	O	A
3-1 Properties of Parallel Lines	✔	✔	✔
• Activity Lab: Parallel Lines and Related Angles	✔	✔	✔
3-2 Proving Lines Parallel	✔	✔	✔
3-3 Parallel and Perpendicular Lines	✔	✔	✔
• Guided Problem Solving: Understanding Proof Problems	✔	✔	✔
3-4 Parallel Lines and the Triangle Angle-Sum Theorem	✔	✔	✔
• Activity Lab: Angle Dynamics	✔	✔	✔
• Activity Lab: Exploring Spherical Geometry			✔
3-5 The Polygon Angle-Sum Theorems	✔	✔	✔
• Activity Lab: Exterior Angles of Polygons	✔	✔	✔
• Algebra 1 Review: Slope	✔	✔	
3-6 Lines in the Coordinate Plane	✔	✔	✔
• Activity Lab: Solving Linear Equations With Graphs and Tables	✔	✔	✔
3-7 Slopes of Parallel and Perpendicular Lines	✔	✔	✔
3-8 Constructing Parallel and Perpendicular Lines	✔	✔	✔
• Activity Lab: Using Tables and Lists		✔	✔
• Activity Lab: Applying Parallel Lines		✔	✔

Chapter 4 Congruent Triangles	B	O	A
4-1 Congruent Figures	✔	✔	✔
4-2 Triangle Congruence by SSS and SAS	✔	✔	✔
• Activity Lab: Building Congruent Triangles	✔	✔	✔
• Vocabulary Builder: High-Use Academic Words		✔	✔
4-3 Triangle Congruence by ASA and AAS	✔	✔	✔
• Activity Lab: Exploring AAA and SSA		✔	✔
4-4 Using Congruent Triangles: CPCTC	✔	✔	✔
• Guided Problem Solving: Analyzing Errors	✔	✔	✔
4-5 Isosceles and Equilateral Triangles	✔	✔	✔
• Activity Lab: Paper-Folding Conjectures	✔	✔	✔
4-6 Congruence in Right Triangles	✔	✔	✔
• Algebra 1 Review: Systems of Linear Equations			✔
4-7 Using Corresponding Parts of Congruent Triangles		✔	✔
• Extension: Writing Flow Proofs:			✔
• Activity Lab: Probability		✔	✔

Leveled Pacing Guide (continued)

Leveled Pacing Guide

B = Below Level   O = On Level   A = Advanced

Chapter 5 Relationships Within Triangles	B	O	A
5-1 Midsegments of Triangles	✔	✔	✔
• Activity Lab: Investigating Midsegments	✔	✔	✔
5-2 Bisectors in Triangles	✔	✔	✔
5-3 Concurrent Lines, Medians, and Altitudes	✔	✔	✔
• Activity Lab: Special Segments in Triangles	✔	✔	✔
5-4 Inverses, Contrapositives, and Indirect Reasoning		✔	✔
• Guided Problem Solving: Understanding Proof Problems		✔	✔
• Algebra 1 Review: Solving Inequalities	✔	✔	
5-5 Inequalities in Triangles	✔	✔	✔
• Activity Lab: Applying Theorems About Triangles		✔	✔

Chapter 6 Quadrilaterals	B	O	A
6-1 Classifying Quadrilaterals	✔	✔	✔
6-2 Properties of Parallelograms	✔	✔	✔
• Guided Problem Solving: Understanding Proof Problems	✔	✔	✔
6-3 Proving That a Quadrilateral is a Parallelogram	✔	✔	✔
• Activity Lab: Geo-Models	✔	✔	✔
6-4 Special Parallelograms	✔	✔	✔
• Activity Lab: Diagonals of Parallelograms	✔	✔	✔
6-5 Trapezoids and Kites	✔	✔	✔
• Activity Lab: Quadrilaterals in Quadrilaterals		✔	✔
6-6 Placing Figures in the Coordinate Plane		✔	✔
6-7 Proofs Using Coordinate Geometry		✔	✔
• Algebra 1 Review: Quadratics		✔	
• Activity Lab: Predicting		✔	✔

Chapter 7 Similarity	B	O	A
7-1 Ratios and Proportions	✔	✔	✔
• Algebra 1 Review: Solving Quadratic Equations	✔	✔	
7-2 Similar Polygons	✔	✔	✔
• Extension: Fractals			✔
7-3 Proving Triangles Similar	✔	✔	✔
• Vocabulary Builder: Abbreviations and Symbols	✔	✔	
• Algebra 1 Review: Simplifying Radicals	✔	✔	
7-4 Similarity in Right Triangles	✔	✔	✔
7-5 Proportions in Triangles	✔	✔	✔
• Guided Problem Solving: Understanding Word Problems	✔	✔	✔
• Activity Lab: Accuracy, Precision in Data Gathering			✔

Leveled Pacing Guide (continued)

B = Below Level   O = On Level   A = Advanced

Chapter 8 Right Triangles and Trigonometry	B	O	A
8-1 The Pythagorean Theorem and Its Converse	✔	✔	✔
• Activity Lab: The Pythagorean Theorem	✔	✔	✔
• Guided Problem Solving: Understanding Word Problems	✔	✔	
8-2 Special Right Triangles	✔	✔	✔
8-3 The Tangent Ratio	✔	✔	✔
• Activity Lab: The Staff and Stadiascope			✔
8-4 Sine and Cosine Ratios	✔	✔	✔
• Activity Lab: Exploring Trigonometric Ratios	✔	✔	✔
8-5 Angles of Elevation and Depression	✔	✔	✔
• Activity Lab: Measuring From Afar	✔	✔	✔
• Guided Problem Solving: Understanding Word Problems	✔	✔	
8-6 Vectors			✔
• Activity Lab: Applying the Pythagorean Theorem			✔

Chapter 9 Transformations	B	O	A
9-1 Translations	✔	✔	✔
9-2 Reflections	✔	✔	✔
• Activity Lab: Paper Folding and Reflections	✔	✔	✔
9-3 Rotations	✔	✔	✔
• Guided Problem Solving: Understanding Math Problems	✔	✔	
• Activity Lab: Tracing-Paper Transformations	✔	✔	✔
9-4 Symmetry	✔	✔	✔
• Vocabulary Builder: Extend and Generalize	✔	✔	
9-5 Dilations			✔
• Extension: Transformations Using Vectors and Matrices			✔
9-6 Compositions of Reflections		✔	✔
• Activity Lab: Kaleidoscopes			✔
9-7 Tessellations	✔	✔	✔
• Activity Lab: Frieze Patterns	✔	✔	✔
• Activity Lab: Applying Translations and Rotations			✔

Leveled Pacing Guide (continued)

B = Below Level   O = On Level   A = Advanced

Chapter 10 Area	B	O	A
10-1 Areas of Parallelograms and Triangles	✔	✔	✔
• Activity Lab: Transforming to Find Area	✔	✔	✔
10-2 Areas of Trapezoids, Rhombuses, and Kites	✔	✔	✔
10-3 Areas of Regular Polygons	✔	✔	✔
• Guided Problem Solving: Understanding Word Problems		✔	✔
10-4 Perimeters and Areas of Similar Figures	✔	✔	✔
10-5 Trigonometry and Area			✔
• Extension: Laws of Sines and Cosines			✔
10-6 Circles and Arcs	✔	✔	✔
• Algebra 1 Review: Dimensional Analysis	✔	✔	
10-7 Areas of Circles and Sectors	✔	✔	✔
• Activity Lab: Exploring Area and Circumference	✔	✔	✔
10-8 Geometric Probability		✔	✔
• Activity Lab: Misleading Graphs		✔	✔

Chapter 11 Surface Area and Volume	B	O	A
11-1 Space Figures and Cross Sections	✔	✔	✔
• Extension: Drawing in Perspective			✔
• Algebra 1 Review: Literal Equations	✔	✔	
11-2 Surface Areas of Prisms and Cylinders	✔	✔	✔
• Guided Problem Solving: Understanding Word Problems		✔	✔
• Activity Lab: Exploring Surface Area	✔	✔	✔
11-3 Surface Areas of Pyramid and Cones	✔	✔	✔
11-4 Volumes of Prisms and Cylinders	✔	✔	✔
11-5 Volumes of Pyramids and Cones	✔	✔	✔
11-6 Surface Areas and Volumes of Spheres	✔	✔	✔
11-7 Areas and Volumes of Similar Solids	✔	✔	✔
• Activity Lab: Exploring Similar Solids		✔	✔
• Activity Lab: Applying Volume		✔	✔

Chapter 12 Circles	B	O	A
12-1 Tangent Lines	✔	✔	✔
12-2 Chords and Arcs	✔	✔	✔
• Activity Lab: Paper Folding With Circles	✔	✔	✔
• Guided Problem Solving: Understanding Math Problems		✔	✔
12-3 Inscribed Angles	✔	✔	✔
12-4 Angle Measures and Segment Lengths		✔	✔
• Activity Lab: Exploring Chords and Secants		✔	✔
• Extension: Tangent Lines, Tangent Ratios			✔
12-5 Circles in the Coordinate Plane		✔	✔
12-6 Locus: A Set of Points			✔
• Activity Lab: Market Research			✔

Pacing Options

These charts suggest pacing only for the core lessons and their parts and they are provided merely as possible guides. They will help you determine how much time you have in your schedule to cover the other features, such as the Activity Labs, Extensions, Guided Problem Solving, and Assessments.

Chapter 1

Schedule	1	2	3	4	5	6	7	8	9	10	11	12	13	14	15	16	17
Traditional (40 to 45 min class periods)	1-1 ▼1	1-2 ▼1	1-2 ▼2	1-3 ▼1	1-3 ▼1	1-3 ▼2	1-4 ▼2	1-4 ▼2	1-5 ▼1	1-6 ▼1	1-6 ▼2	1-7 ▼2	1-7 ▼2	1-8 ▼1	1-8 ▼1	1-9 ▼1	1-9 ▼2
Two-Year Geometry (40 to 45 min class periods)	1-1 ▼1	1-1 ▼2	1-2 ▼2	1-3 ▼1	1-3 ▼2	1-4 ▼2	1-4 ▼1	1-4 ▼2	1-5 ▼1	1-6 ▼1	1-6 ▼2	1-7 ▼2	1-7 ▼2	1-8 ▼1	1-8 ▼2	1-9 ▼1	1-9 ▼2
Block Scheduling (90 min class periods)	1-1 ▼1,2	1-2 ▼1,2	1-3 ▼1	1-4 ▼1,2	1-5 ▼1	1-6 ▼1,2	1-7 ▼1,2	1-8 ▼1,2	1-9 ▼1,2								

Chapter 2

Schedule	1	2	3	4	5	6	7	8	9	10
Traditional (40 to 45 min class periods)	2-1 ▼2	2-2 ▼1	2-2 ▼2	2-3 ▼1	2-3 ▼2	2-3 ▼1	2-4 ▼1	2-5 ▼1		
Two-Year Geometry (40 to 45 min class periods)	2-1 ▼1	2-1 ▼2	2-1 ▼2	2-2 ▼2	2-2 ▼1	2-2 ▼2	2-3 ▼2	2-3 ▼2	2-4 ▼1	2-5 ▼1
Block Scheduling (90 min class periods)	2-1 ▼1,2	2-2 ▼2	2-3 ▼1	2-4 ▼1	2-5 ▼1					

Chapter 3

Schedule	1	2	3	4	5	6	7	8	9	10	11	12	13	14	15	16
Traditional (40 to 45 min class periods)	3-1 ▼1	3-1 ▼2	3-2 ▼1	3-3 ▼1	3-4 ▼1	3-4 ▼2	3-5 ▼1	3-5 ▼2	3-5 ▼1	3-6 ▼1	3-6 ▼2	3-7 ▼1	3-7 ▼2	3-8 ▼1	3-8 ▼2	
Two-Year Geometry (40 to 45 min class periods)	3-1 ▼1	3-1 ▼2	3-2 ▼2	3-3 ▼1	3-4 ▼1	3-4 ▼1	3-4 ▼2	3-5 ▼2	3-5 ▼2	3-6 ▼1	3-6 ▼2	3-7 ▼1	3-7 ▼2	3-7 ▼2	3-8 ▼1	3-8 ▼2
Block Scheduling (90 min class periods)	3-2 ▼1	3-3 ▼1	3-4 ▼1	3-5 ▼1,2	3-6 ▼1,2	3-7 ▼1,2	3-8 ▼1,2									

Pacing Options (continued)

CH 4

	1 Class Period	1 Class Period	1 Class Period	1 Class Period	1 Class Period	1 Class Period	1 Class Period	1 Class Period	1 Class Period	1 Class Period	1 Class Period	1 Class Period	1 Class Period
Traditional 40 to 45 min class periods	4-1 ▼1	4-2 ▼1	4-3 ▼1	4-4 ▼1	4-5 ▼1	4-6 ▼1	4-7 ▼1	4-7 ▼2					
Two-Year Geometry 40 to 45 min class periods	4-1 ▼1	4-1 ▼1	4-2 ▼1	4-2 ▼1	4-3 ▼1	4-3 ▼1	4-4 ▼1	4-4 ▼1	4-5 ▼1	4-6 ▼1	4-6 ▼1	4-7 ▼1	4-7 ▼2
Block Scheduling 90 min class periods	4-1 ▼1	4-2 ▼1	4-3 ▼1	4-4 ▼1	4-5 ▼1	4-6 ▼1	4-7 ▼1,2						

CH 5

	1 Class Period	1 Class Period	1 Class Period	1 Class Period	1 Class Period	1 Class Period	1 Class Period	1 Class Period	1 Class Period	1 Class Period	1 Class Period	1 Class Period	1 Class Period
Traditional 40 to 45 min class periods	5-1 ▼1	5-2 ▼1	5-3 ▼1	5-3 ▼2	5-5 ▼1	5-5 ▼2							
Two-Year Geometry 40 to 45 min class periods	5-1 ▼1	5-2 ▼1	5-2 ▼1	5-3 ▼1	5-3 ▼2	5-3 ▼2	5-5 ▼1	5-5 ▼2	5-5 ▼2				
Block Scheduling 90 min class periods	5-1 ▼1	5-2 ▼1	5-3 ▼1,2	5-5 ▼1,2									

CH 6

	1 Class Period	1 Class Period	1 Class Period	1 Class Period	1 Class Period	1 Class Period	1 Class Period	1 Class Period	1 Class Period	1 Class Period	1 Class Period	1 Class Period	1 Class Period
Traditional 40 to 45 min class periods	6-1 ▼1	6-2 ▼1	6-2 ▼2	6-3 ▼1	6-4 ▼1	6-4 ▼2	6-5 ▼1						
Two-Year Geometry 40 to 45 min class periods	6-1 ▼1	6-2 ▼1	6-2 ▼1	6-2 ▼2	6-2 ▼2	6-3 ▼1	6-4 ▼1	6-4 ▼2	6-4 ▼2	6-5 ▼1	6-5 ▼2		
Block Scheduling 90 min class periods	6-1 ▼1	6-2 ▼1,2	6-3 ▼1	6-4 ▼1,2	6-5 ▼1								

Informal Geometry Lesson Plans and Assessments

Pacing Options (continued)

CH 7

	1 Class Period	1 Class Period	1 Class Period	1 Class Period	1 Class Period	1 Class Period	1 Class Period	1 Class Period	1 Class Period	1 Class Period	1 Class Period	1 Class Period	1 Class Period
Traditional 40 to 45 min class periods	7-1 ▼1	7-2 ▼1	7-2 ▼2	7-3 ▼1	7-3 ▼2	7-4 ▼1	7-5 ▼1	7-5 ▼2					
Two-Year Geometry 40 to 45 min class periods	7-1 ▼1	7-1 ▼1	7-2 ▼1	7-2 ▼2	7-2 ▼2	7-3 ▼1	7-3 ▼2	7-3 ▼2	7-4 ▼1	7-4 ▼1	7-5 ▼1	7-5 ▼1	7-5 ▼2
Block Scheduling 90 min class periods	7-1 ▼1	7-2 ▼1,2	7-3 ▼1	7-4 ▼1	7-5 ▼1,2								

CH 8

	1 Class Period	1 Class Period	1 Class Period	1 Class Period	1 Class Period	1 Class Period	1 Class Period	1 Class Period	1 Class Period	1 Class Period	1 Class Period	1 Class Period	1 Class Period
Traditional 40 to 45 min class periods	8-1 ▼1	8-2 ▼1	8-2 ▼2	8-3 ▼1	8-4 ▼1	8-5 ▼1	8-5 ▼1						
Two-Year Geometry 40 to 45 min class periods	8-1 ▼1	8-1 ▼2	8-1 ▼2	8-2 ▼1	8-2 ▼2	8-3 ▼1	8-3 ▼1	8-4 ▼1	8-4 ▼1	8-5 ▼1	8-5 ▼1		
Block Scheduling 90 min class periods	8-2 ▼1	8-3 ▼1	8-4 ▼1	8-4 ▼1	8-5 ▼1								

CH 9

	1 Class Period	1 Class Period	1 Class Period	1 Class Period	1 Class Period	1 Class Period	1 Class Period	1 Class Period	1 Class Period	1 Class Period	1 Class Period	1 Class Period	1 Class Period
Traditional 40 to 45 min class periods	9-1 ▼2	9-2 ▼1	9-3 ▼1	9-3 ▼1	9-4 ▼1	9-4 ▼1	9-7 ▼1	9-7 ▼2					
Two-Year Geometry 40 to 45 min class periods	9-1 ▼1	9-1 ▼2	9-2 ▼1	9-2 ▼1	9-3 ▼1	9-3 ▼1	9-4 ▼1	9-4 ▼1	9-4 ▼1	9-7 ▼1	9-7 ▼2		
Block Scheduling 90 min class periods	9-1 ▼1,2	9-3 ▼1	9-4 ▼1	9-7 ▼1,2									

Pacing Options (continued)

CH 10

	1 Class Period	1 Class Period	1 Class Period	1 Class Period	1 Class Period	1 Class Period	1 Class Period	1 Class Period	1 Class Period	1 Class Period	1 Class Period	1 Class Period	1 Class Period	1 Class Period	1 Class Period
Traditional 40 to 45 min class periods	10-1 ▼1	10-1 ▼2	10-2 ▼1	10-2 ▼2	10-3 ▼1	10-4 ▼1	10-4 ▼1	10-6 ▼1	10-6 ▼2	10-6 ▼2	10-6 ▼1	10-6 ▼2	10-6 ▼2	10-7 ▼1	10-7 ▼1
Two-Year Geometry 40 to 45 min class periods	10-1 ▼1	10-1 ▼2	10-2 ▼1	10-2 ▼2	10-3 ▼1	10-4 ▼1	10-4 ▼1	10-4 ▼1	10-6 ▼2	10-6 ▼2	10-6 ▼2	10-7 ▼1	10-7 ▼1	10-8 ▼1	
Block Scheduling 90 min class periods	10-1 ▼1,2	10-2 ▼1	10-3 ▼1	10-4 ▼1	10-6 ▼1,2	10-7 ▼1									

CH 11

	1 Class Period	1 Class Period	1 Class Period	1 Class Period	1 Class Period	1 Class Period	1 Class Period	1 Class Period	1 Class Period	1 Class Period	1 Class Period	1 Class Period	1 Class Period	1 Class Period	1 Class Period	1 Class Period	1 Class Period	1 Class Period
Traditional 40 to 45 min class periods	11-1 ▼1	11-1 ▼2	11-2 ▼1	11-2 ▼2	11-3 ▼1	11-3 ▼1	11-3 ▼2	11-3 ▼2	11-4 ▼1	11-4 ▼2	11-4 ▼1	11-4 ▼1	11-5 ▼2	11-5 ▼1	11-6 ▼1			
Two-Year Geometry 40 to 45 min class periods	11-1 ▼1	11-1 ▼2	11-1 ▼2	11-2 ▼1	11-2 ▼2	11-2 ▼2	11-3 ▼1	11-3 ▼2	11-3 ▼2	11-4 ▼2	11-4 ▼2	11-4 ▼1	11-4 ▼2	11-4 ▼2	11-5 ▼1	11-5 ▼2	11-6 ▼1	11-6 ▼1
Block Scheduling 90 min class periods	11-1 ▼1,2	11-2 ▼1,2	11-3 ▼1,2	11-4 ▼1,2	11-5 ▼1,2	11-6 ▼1												

CH 12

	1 Class Period	1 Class Period	1 Class Period	1 Class Period	1 Class Period	1 Class Period	1 Class Period	1 Class Period	1 Class Period	1 Class Period
Traditional 40 to 45 min class periods	12-1 ▼1	12-2 ▼1	12-2 ▼2	12-3 ▼1	12-3 ▼1	12-3 ▼2	12-5 ▼1	12-5 ▼2		
Two-Year Geometry 40 to 45 min class periods	12-1 ▼1	12-1 ▼2	12-2 ▼1	12-2 ▼2	12-2 ▼2	12-3 ▼1	12-3 ▼2	12-3 ▼2	12-3 ▼1	12-5 ▼2
Block Scheduling 90 min class periods	12-1 ▼1,2	12-2 ▼1,2	12-3 ▼1,2	12-5 ▼1,2						

Informal Geometry Lesson Plans and Assessments

Lesson 1-1

Patterns and Inductive Reasoning

INTRODUCE

Check Skills You'll Need (p. 4)
Students review lists involving even and odd numbers, and perfect squares.

FACILITATE

Math Background (p. 4)
Remind students that when making a conjecture, they only need one counterexample to disprove the conjecture.

Quick Check questions (pp. 4–6)
Assign these questions after each Example to see whether students understand the concepts presented.

Objectives
▼ Use inductive reasoning to make conjectures

New Vocabulary
inductive reasoning, conjecture, counterexample

Standards
- NCTM Standards: Number and Operations, Problem Solving, Reasoning and Proof, Communication, Connections, Representation

	Informal Geometry Course	**Optional Material**
Teaching Guide	▼ *Using Inductive Reasoning* (pp. 4–6) **Example 1:** Finding and Using a Pattern **Example 2:** Using Inductive Reasoning **Example 3:** Finding a Counterexample **Example 4:** Real-World Connection TE: Additional Examples 1–4, page 5	
Assignment Guide	▼ Informal Geometry Exercises: 1–31, 34	▼ Exercises: 32, 33, 35–53 Extension: 54, 55
Assessment	Test Prep: Exercises 56–59 Mixed Review: Exercises 60–62 TE: Lesson Quiz: 1-1	

RESOURCE OPTIONS

Teaching Resources	Chapter 1 Grab & Go File:
	    Practice 1-1, Reteaching 1-1,
	    Enrichment 1-1
	Spanish Vocabulary Workbook and Study Skills
		All-in-One Student Workbook 1-1
		Spanish Practice Workbook
		Hands-On Activities 1

Transparencies	Check Skills You'll Need 1-1 Additional Examples 1-1 Test-Taking Strategies 1, with practice sheet	Lesson Quiz 1-1 Student Edition Answers 1-1
Technology	Interactive Textbook Online ExamView Assessment Suite Teacher Express Presentation Express with QuickTake	Worksheets Online Success Tracker Online Intervention

Lesson 1-2

Drawings, Nets, and Other Models

INTRODUCE

Check Skills You'll Need (p. 10)
Students determine the next figure in a geometric sequence.

FACILITATE

Math Background (p. 10)
Discuss with students how isometric dot paper can show the vertices and faces of three-dimensional figures.

Quick Check questions (pp. 10–12)
Assign these questions after each Example to see whether students understand the concepts presented.

Objectives
▼ Make isometric and orthographic drawings
▼ Draw nets for three-dimensional figures

New Vocabulary
isometric drawing, orthographic drawing, foundation drawing, net

Standards
- NCTM Standards: Geometry, Problem Solving, Reasoning and Proof, Communication, Connections, Representation

	Informal Geometry Course	Optional Material
Teaching Guide	▼*Drawing Isometric and Orthographic Views* (pp. 10–11) **Example 1:** Isometric Drawing **Example 2:** Orthographic Drawing **Example 3:** Foundation Drawing ▼*Nets for Three-Dimensional Figures* (p. 12) **Example 4:** Identifying Solids From Nets **Example 5:** Drawing a Net TE: Additional Examples 1–5, pages 11–12	
Assignment Guide	▼Informal Geometry Exercises: 1–10, 18–20 ▼Informal Geometry Exercises: 11–16, 23–26	▼Exercises: 17, 21, 22, 28–30 Extension: 33 ▼Exercises: 27, 31–32 Extension: 34
Assessment	Test Prep: Exercises 35–38 Mixed Review: Exercises 39–45 TE: Lesson Quiz: 1-2	

RESOURCE OPTIONS

Teaching Resources	Chapter 1 Grab & Go File:
	    Practice 1-2, Reteaching 1-2,
	    Enrichment 1-2
	Spanish Vocabulary Workbook and Study Skills
		All-in-One Student Workbook 1-2
		Spanish Practice Workbook
		Hands-On Activities 2

Transparencies	Check Skills You'll Need 1-2 Additional Examples 1-2 Test-Taking Strategies 1, with practice sheet	Lesson Quiz 1-2 Student Edition Answers 1-2
Technology	Interactive Textbook Online ExamView Assessment Suite Teacher Express Presentation Express with QuickTake	Worksheets Online Success Tracker Online Intervention

Lesson 1-3

Points, Lines, and Planes

INTRODUCE

Check Skills You'll Need (p. 16)
Students review systems of equations and the basics of points, lines, and planes.

Hands-On Activity (p. 16)
Constellations are used to help students discover a pattern in the number of lines that can be drawn through a given number of points.

FACILITATE

Math Background (p. 16)
Discuss with students the value and trueness of points, lines, and planes to the foundation of geometry.

Quick Check questions (pp. 17–19)
Assign these questions after each Example to see whether students understand the concepts presented.

Objectives
▼ Understand basic terms of geometry
▼ Understand basic postulates of geometry

New Vocabulary
point, space, line, collinear points, plane, coplanar, postulate, axiom

Standards
• NCTM Standards: Geometry, Problem Solving, Reasoning and Proof, Communication, Connections, Representation

	Informal Geometry Course	Optional Material
Teaching Guide	▼ *Basic Terms of Geometry* (pp. 16–17) **Example 1:** Identifying Collinear Points **Example 2:** Naming a Plane ▼ *Basic Postulates of Geometry* (pp. 18–19) **Example 3:** Finding the Intersection of Two Planes **Example 4:** Using Postulate 1-4 TE: Additional Examples 1–4, pages 17–18	
Assignment Guide	▼ Informal Geometry Exercises: 1–16 ▼ Informal Geometry Exercises: 17–45	▼ Exercises: 46–60, 64, 68–73, Extension: 74, 77–79 ▼ Exercises: 61–63, 65–67 Extension: 75, 76
Assessment	Test Prep: Exercises 80–84 Mixed Review: Exercises 85–90 TE: Lesson Quiz: 1-3	

RESOURCE OPTIONS

Teaching Resources	Chapter 1 Grab & Go File:
	    Practice 1-3, Reteaching 1-3,
	    Enrichment 1-3
	Spanish Vocabulary Workbook and Study Skills
		All-in-One Student Workbook 1-3
		Spanish Practice Workbook
		Hands-On Activities 2

Transparencies	Check Skills You'll Need 1-3 Additional Examples 1-3 Test-Taking Strategies 1, with practice sheet	Lesson Quiz 1-3 Student Edition Answers 1-3
Technology	Interactive Textbook Online ExamView Assessment Suite Teacher Express Presentation Express with QuickTake	Worksheets Online Success Tracker Online Intervention

Lesson 1-4

Segments, Rays, Parallel Lines and Planes

INTRODUCE

• **Check Skills You'll Need** (p. 23)
Students determine whether two given lines will intersect and review naming planes.

FACILITATE

Math Background (p. 23)
Discuss with students new terms in this lesson (ray, segment, parallel lines) that can be derived from the three basic terms in the previous lesson (point, line, plane).

Quick Check questions (pp. 23–25)
Assign these questions after each Example to see whether students understand the concepts presented.

Objectives
▼ Identify segments and rays
▼ Recognize parallel lines

New Vocabulary
segment, ray, opposite rays, parallel lines, skew lines, parallel planes

Standards
• NCTM Standards: Geometry, Problem Solving, Communication, Connections, Representation

	Informal Geometry Course	Optional Material
Teaching Guide	▼ *Identifying Segments and Rays* (p. 23) **Example 1:** Naming Segments and Rays ▼ *Recognizing Parallel Lines and Planes* (pp. 24–25) **Example 2:** Identifying Parallel and Skew Segments **Example 3:** Identifying Parallel Planes TE: Additional Examples 1–3, pages 24–25	
Assignment Guide	▼ Informal Geometry Exercises: 1–3, 34 ▼ Informal Geometry Exercises: 4–33	▼ Exercises: 35, 36 Extension: 40 ▼ Exercises: 37–39 Extension: 41–45
Assessment	Test Prep: Exercises 46–50 Mixed Review: Exercise 51–66 Checkpoint Quiz 1 TE: Lesson Quiz: 1-4	

RESOURCE OPTIONS

Teaching Resources	Chapter 1 Grab & Go File:
	    Practice 1-4, Reteaching 1-4,
	    Enrichment 1-4
	Spanish Vocabulary Workbook and Study Skills
		All-in-One Student Workbook 1-4
		Spanish Practice Workbook
		Hands-On Activities 3

Transparencies	Check Skills You'll Need 1-4 Additional Examples 1-4 Test-Taking Strategies 1, with practice sheet	Lesson Quiz 1-4 Student Edition Answers 1-4
Technology	Interactive Textbook Online ExamView Assessment Suite Teacher Express Presentation Express with QuickTake	Worksheets Online Success Tracker Online Intervention

Lesson 1-5

Measuring Segments

INTRODUCE

Check Skills You'll Need (p. 31)
Students review absolute value and solving multistep equations.

FACILITATE

Math Background (p. 31)
Discuss with students in further detail how the abstract descriptions of the Ruler Postulate and Protractor Postulate truly define how we commonly use rulers and protractors.

Quick Check questions (pp. 32–33)
Assign these questions after each Example to see whether students understand the concepts presented.

Objectives
▼ Find the lengths of segments

New Vocabulary
coordinate, congruent segments, midpoint

Standards
• NCTM Standards: Number and Operations, Algebra, Geometry, Measurement, Problem Solving, Reasoning and Proof, Communication, Connections, Representation

	Informal Geometry Course	**Optional Material**
Teaching Guide	▼ *Finding Segment Lengths* (pp. 31–33) **Example 1:** Comparing Segment Lengths **Example 2:** Using the Segment Addition Postulate **Example 3:** Using the Midpoint TE: Additional Examples 1–3, pages 33–34	*Algebra 1 Review: Solving Linear Equations* (p. 30)
Assignment Guide	▼Informal Geometry Exercises: 1–19	▼Exercises: 20–35 Extension: 36–38
Assessment	Test Prep: Exercises 39–44 Mixed Review: Exercises 45–55 TE: Lesson Quiz: 1-5	

RESOURCE OPTIONS

Teaching Resources	Chapter 1 Grab & Go File:
	     Practice 1-5, Reteaching 1-5,
	     Enrichment 1-5
	 Spanish Vocabulary Workbook and Study Skills
		All-in-One Student Workbook 1-5
		 Spanish Practice Workbook

Transparencies	Check Skills You'll Need 1-5 Additional Examples 1-5 Classroom Aid, *Protractor* Test-Taking Strategies 1, with practice sheet	Lesson Quiz 1-5 Student Edition Answers 1-5
Technology	Interactive Textbook Online ExamView Assessment Suite Teacher Express Presentation Express with QuickTake	Worksheets Online Success Tracker Online Intervention

Lesson 1-6

Meausuring Angles

NTRODUCE

Check Skills You'll Need (p. 36)
Students review solving linear equations.

FACILITATE

Math Background (p. 36)
Discuss with students the similarities between the Angle Addition Postulate and the Segment Addition Postulate.
Quick Check questions (pp. 36–39)
Assign these questions after each Example to see whether students understand the concepts presented.

Objectives
▼ Find the measure of angles
▼ Identify special angle pairs

New Vocabulary
angle, acute angle, right angle, obtuse angle, straight angle, congruent angles, vertical angles, complementary angles, supplementary angles

Standards
- NCTM Standards: Geometry, Measurement, Problem Solving, Communication, Connections, Representation

	Informal Geometry Course	Optional Material
Teaching Guide	▼ *Finding Angle Measures* (pp. 36–38) **Example 1:** Naming Angles **Example 2:** Measuring and Classifying Angles **Example 3:** Using the Angle Addition Postulate ▼ *Identifying Angle Pairs* (pp. 38–39) **Example 4:** Identifying Angle Pairs **Example 5:** Making Conclusions From a Diagram TE: Additional Examples 1–5, pages 37–39	
Assignment Guide	▼ Informal Geometry Exercises: 1–14, 33, 34 ▼ Informal Geometry Exercises: 15–32	▼ Exercises: 35–47 Extension: 49 ▼ Extension: 48
Assessment	Test Prep: Exercises 50–54 Mixed Review: Exercises 55–59 TE: Lesson Quiz: 1-6	

RESOURCE OPTIONS

Teaching Resources	Chapter 1 Grab & Go File:
	  Practice 1-6, Reteaching 1-6,
	  Enrichment 1-6
	 Spanish Vocabulary Workbook and Study Skills
		All-in-One Student Workbook 1-6
		 Spanish Practice Workbook

Transparencies	Check Skills You'll Need 1-6 Additional Examples 1-6 Test-Taking Strategies 1, with practice sheet	Lesson Quiz 1-6 Student Edition Answers 1-1
Technology	Interactive Textbook Online ExamView Assessment Suite Teacher Express Presentation Express with QuickTake	Worksheets Online Success Tracker Online Intervention

Lesson 1-7

Basic Constructions

INTRODUCE

Check Skills You'll Need (p. 44)
Students practice drawing basic geometric elements that will be used as a basis for more complex constructions later in the lesson.

FACILITATE

Math Background (p. 44)
Remind students of the importance of compass-and-straightedge constructions to the justification of many geometric postulates and theorems.

Quick Check questions (pp. 44–47)
Assign these questions after each Example to see whether students understand the concepts presented.

Objectives
▼ Use a compass and a straightedge to construct congruent segments and congruent angles
▼ Use a compass and a straightedge to bisect segments and angles

New Vocabulary
construction, straightedge, compass, perpendicular lines, perpendicular bisector, angle bisector

Standards
• NCTM Standards: Geometry, Measurement, Problem Solving, Communication, Connections, Representation

	Informal Geometry Course	Optional Material
Teaching Guide	▼ *Constructing Segments and Angles* (pp. 44–45) **Example 1:** Constructing Congruent Segments **Example 2:** Constructing Congruent Angles ▼ *Constructing Bisectors* (pp. 45–47) **Example 3:** Constructing the Perpendicular Bisector **Example 4:** Finding Angle Measures **Example 5:** Constructing the Angle Bisector TE: Additional Examples 1–5, pages 45–46	Activity Lab: *Hands-On: Compass Designs* (p. 43) Activity Lab: *Technology: Exploring Constructions* (p. 51)
Assignment Guide	▼ Informal Geometry Exercises: 1–6, 15 ▼ Informal Geometry Exercises: 7–14, 26, 27	▼ Exercises: 22–24, 29–32, 34 ▼ Exercises: 16–21, 25, 28, 33; Extension: 35, 36
Assessment	Test Prep: Exercises 37–40 Mixed Review: Exercises 41–50 TE: Lesson Quiz: 1-7	

RESOURCE OPTIONS

Teaching Resources	Chapter 1 Grab & Go File: 　Practice 1-7, Reteaching 1-7, 　Enrichment 1-7 Spanish Vocabulary Workbook and Study Skills	All-in-One Student Workbook 1-7 Spanish Practice Workbook
Transparencies	Check Skills You'll Need 1-7 Additional Examples 1-7 Test-Taking Strategies 1, with practice sheet	Lesson Quiz 1-7 Student Edition Answers 1-7
Technology	Interactive Textbook Online ExamView Assessment Suite Teacher Express Presentation Express with QuickTake	Worksheets Online Success Tracker Online Intervention

Lesson 1-8

The Coordinate Plane

INTRODUCE

Activity Lab (p. 52)
Students use a map of New York City to explore distance in a real-world example of the coordinate plane. They also experience using a scale to determine actual distances.

Check Skills You'll Need (p. 53)
Students review square roots and evaluate expressions.

FACILITATE

Math Background (p. 53)
Discuss with students how the Distance Formula and Midpoint Formula are derived from the Ruler Postulate.

Quick Check questions (pp. 54–55)
Assign these after each Example to see whether students understand the concepts presented.

<table>
<tr><td colspan="2">Objectives
▼ Find the distance between two points in the coordinate plane
▼ Find the coordinates of the midpoint of a segment in the coordinate plane</td></tr>
<tr><td colspan="2">New Vocabulary
none</td></tr>
<tr><td colspan="2">Standards
• NCTM Standards: Number and Operation, Algebra, Geometry, Measurement, Problem Solving, Communication, Connections, Representation</td></tr>
</table>

	Informal Geometry Course	Optional Material
Teaching Guide	▼ *Finding Distance on the Coordinate Plane* (pp. 53–54) **Example 1:** Finding Distance **Example 2:** Real-World Connection ▼ *Finding the Midpoint of a Segment* (pp. 54–55) **Example 3:** Finding the Midpoint **Example 4:** Finding an Endpoint TE: Additional Examples 1–4, page 54	Activity Lab: *Hands-On: Distance in the Coordinate Plane* (p. 52) *Guided Problem Solving* (p. 52)
Assignment Guide	▼ Informal Geometry Exercises: 1–17, 47, 48 ▼ Informal Geometry Exercises: 18–40, 43, 45	▼ Exercises: 49–56 Extension: 57, 58, 60–63 ▼ Exercises: 41, 42, 44, 46 Extension: 59
Assessment	Test Prep: Exercises 64–69 Mixed Review: Exercises 70–78 Checkpoint Quiz 2 TE: Lesson Quiz: 1-8	

RESOURCE OPTIONS

Teaching Resources	Chapter 1 Grab & Go File:
	   Practice 1-8, Reteaching 1-8,
	   Enrichment 1-8
	Spanish Vocabulary Workbook and Study Skills
		All-in-One Student Workbook 1-8
		Spanish Practice Workbook

Transparencies	Check Skills You'll Need 1-8 Additional Examples 1-8 Classroom Aid, *Coordinate Plane* and *Quarter-inch Graph Paper* Test-Taking Strategies 1, with practice sheet	Lesson Quiz 1-8 Student Edition Answers 1-8
Technology	Interactive Textbook Online ExamView Assessment Suite Teacher Express Presentation Express with QuickTake	Worksheets Online Success Tracker Online Intervention

Lesson 1-9

Perimeter, Circumference, and Area

INTRODUCE

Check Skills You'll Need (p. 61)
Students evaluate absolute value expressions and
calculate the distance between two given points.

Hands-On Activity (p. 61)
Students use grid paper to find perimeter and
area and thus discover that equal perimeters do
no imply equal areas.

FACILITATE

Math Background (p. 61)
Discuss with students the difference between a
polygon and a polygonal region.

Quick Check questions (pp. 62–64)
Assign these after each Example to see whether
students understand the concepts presented.

Objectives
▼ Find perimeters of rectangles and squares
and circumferences of circles
▼ Find areas of rectangles, squares, and circles

New Vocabulary
none

Standards
• NCTM Standards: Number and Operations,
Algebra, Geometry, Measurement, Problem
Solving, Communication, Connections,
Representation

	Informal Geometry Course	Optional Material
Teaching Guide	▼*Finding Perimeter and Circumference* (pp. 61–63) **Example 1:** Real-World Connection **Example 2:** Finding Circumference **Example 3:** Finding Perimeter in the Coordinate Plane ▼*Finding Area* (pp. 63–64) **Example 4:** Finding Area of a Rectangle **Example 5:** Finding Area of a Circle **Example 6:** Finding Area of an Irregular Shape TE: Additional Examples 1–6, pages 62–64	*Technology: Comparing Perimeters and Areas* (p. 69)
Assignment Guide	▼Informal Geometry Exercises: 1–19 ▼Informal Geometry Exercises: 20–47, 49, 56–59	▼Exercises: 50, 55 Extension: 70 ▼Exercises: 48, 51–54, 60–63; Extension: 64–67
Assessment	Test Prep: Exercises 71–75 Mixed Review: Exercises 76–88 TE: Lesson Quiz: 1-9	Ch. Review (pp. 71–73) Chapter Test (p. 74) Stand. Test Prep (p. 75)

RESOURCE OPTIONS

Teaching Resources	Chapter 1 Grab & Go File:
	   Practice 1-9, Reteaching 1-9,
	   Enrichment 1-9
	Chapter 1 Test, Forms F and G
	Spanish Vocabulary Workbook and Study Skills
		All-in-One Student Workbook 1-9
		Spanish Practice Workbook
		Alternative Assessment, Form C
		Geometry Test Preparation

Transparencies	Check Skills You'll Need 1-9 Additional Examples 1-9 Classroom Aid, *Spreadsheet, Square dot Paper,* and *Problem Solving Strategies* Test-Taking Strategies 1, with practice sheet	Lesson Quiz 1-9 Student Edition Answers 1-9
Technology	Interactive Textbook Online ExamView Assessment Suite Teacher Express Presentation Express with QuickTake	Worksheets Online Success Tracker Online Intervention Mindpoint Quiz Show

Lesson 2-1

Conditional Statements

INTRODUCE

Check Skills You'll Need (p. 80)
Students review solving one-step equations.

FACILITATE

Math Background (p. 80)
Discuss with students how the truth value of a conditional is based on the truth values of its hypothesis and conclusion.

Quick Check questions (pp. 80–82)
Assign these questions after each Example to see whether students understand the concepts presented.

Objectives
▼ Recognize conditional statements
▼ Write converses of conditional statements

New Vocabulary
conditional, hypothesis, conclusion, truth value, converse

Standards
• NCTM Standards: Algebra, Geometry, Problem Solving, Reasoning and Proof, Communication, Connections, Representation

	Informal Geometry Course	Optional Material
Teaching Guide	▼*Conditional Statements* (pp. 80–81) **Example 1:** Identifying the Hypothesis and the Conclusion **Example 2:** Writing a Conditional **Example 3:** Finding a Counterexample **Example 4:** Using a Venn Diagram ▼*Converses* (pp. 81–82) **Example 5:** Writing the Converse of a Conditional **Example 6:** Finding the Truth Value of a Converse **Example 7:** Real-World Connection TE: Additional Examples 1–7, pages 81–82	
Assignment Guide	▼Informal Geometry Exercises: 1–22, 33–35, 40 ▼Informal Geometry Exercises: 23–32, 41–48	▼Exercises: 38, 39, 52–58 Extension: 59–61 ▼Exercises: 36, 37, 47–51 Extension: 62, 63
Assessment Guide	Test Prep: Exercises 64–67 Mixed Review: Exercises 68–78 TE: Lesson Quiz: 2-1	

RESOURCE OPTIONS

Teaching Resources	Chapter 2 Grab & Go File:
	   Practice 2-1, Reteaching 2-1,
	   Enrichment 2-1
	Spanish Vocabulary Workbook and Study Skills
		All-in-One Student Workbook 2-1
		Spanish Practice Workbook
		Hands-On Activities 4

Transparencies	Check Skills You'll Need 2-1 Additional Examples 2-1 Test-Taking Strategies 2, with practice sheet	Lesson Quiz 2-1 Student Edition Answers 2-1
Technology	Interactive Textbook Online ExamView Assessment Suite Teacher Express Presentation Express with QuickTake	Worksheets Online Success Tracker Online Intervention

Lesson 2-2

Biconditionals and Definitions

INTRODUCE

Check Skills You'll Need (p. 87)
Students review identifying the hypothesis and conclusion and writing conditionals and converses.

Activity (p. 88)
Students use an illustration to help identify and write a good definition of *polyglobs*.

FACILITATE

Math Background (p. 87)
Discuss with students that mathematical definitions are strict in the sense that both the conditional and converse must be true.

Quick Check questions (pp. 87–89)
Assign these questions after each Example to see whether students understand the concepts presented.

Objectives
▼ Write biconditionals
▼ Recognize good definitions

New Vocabulary
biconditional

Standards
- NCTM Standards: Geometry, Problem Solving, Reasoning and Proof, Communication, Connections, Representation

	Informal Geometry Course	Optional Material
Teaching Guide	▼*Writing Biconditionals* (pp. 87–88) **Example 1:** Writing a Biconditional **Example 2:** Separating a Biconditional Into Parts ▼*Recognizing Good Definitions* (pp. 88–89) **Example 3:** Writing a Definition as a Biconditional **Example 4:** Real-World Connection TE: Additional Examples 1–4, pages 88–89	
Assignment Guide	▼Informal Geometry Exercises: 1–12, 32, 33, 34 ▼Informal Geometry Exercises: 13–23, 27	▼Exercises: 38–46 Extension: 47 ▼Exercises: 24–26, 28–31, 35–37 Extension: 48, 49
Assessment Guide	Test Prep: Exercises 50–54 Mixed Review: Exercises 55–69 TE: Lesson Quiz: 2-2	

RESOURCE OPTIONS

Teaching Resources	Chapter 2 Grab & Go File:
	   Practice 2-2, Reteaching 2-2,
	   Enrichment 2-2
	Spanish Vocabulary Workbook and Study Skills
		All-in-One Student Workbook 2-2
		Spanish Practice Workbook

Transparencies	Check Skills You'll Need 2-2 Additional Examples 2-2 Test-Taking Strategies 2, with practice sheet	Lesson Quiz 2-2 Student Edition Answers 2-2
Technology	Interactive Textbook Online ExamView Assessment Suite Teacher Express Presentation Express with QuickTake	Worksheets Online Success Tracker Online Intervention

Lesson 2-3

Deductive Reasoning

INTRODUCE

Check Skills You'll Need (p. 94)
Students review writing converses and conditionals.

FACILITATE

Math Background (p. 94)
Explain to students how almost every line of a two-column proof uses the Law of Detachment.

Quick Check questions (pp. 94–96)
Assign these questions after each Example to see whether students understand the concepts presented.

Objectives
▼ Use the Law of Detachment
▼ Use the Law of Syllogism

New Vocabulary
deductive reasoning, Law of Detachment, Law of Syllogism

Standards
• NCTM Standards: Geometry, Problem Solving, Reasoning and Proof, Communication, Connections, Representation

	Informal Geometry Course	Optional Material
Teaching Guide	▼ *Using the Law of Detachment* (pp. 94–95) **Example 1:** Real-World Connection **Example 2:** Using the Law of Detachment **Example 3:** Real-World Connection ▼ *Using the Law of Syllogism* (pp. 95–96) **Example 4:** Using the Law of Syllogism **Example 5:** Real-World Connection TE: Additional Examples 1–5, pages 95–96	Activity Lab: *Mathematical Systems* (p. 101)
Assignment Guide	▼ Informal Geometry Exercises: 1–9, 22 ▼ Informal Geometry Exercises: 10–15	▼ Exercises: 23–26 ▼ Exercises: 16–21, 27–32 Extension: 33
Assessment Guide	Test Prep: Exercises 34–37 Mixed Review: Exercises 38–44 Checkpoint Quiz 1 TE: Lesson Quiz: 2-3	

RESOURCE OPTIONS

Teaching Resources	Chapter 2 Grab & Go File:
	    Practice 2-3, Reteaching 2-3,
	    Enrichment 2-3
	Spanish Vocabulary Workbook and Study Skills
		All-in-One Student Workbook 2-3
		Spanish Practice Workbook
		Hands-On Activities 5

Transparencies	Check Skills You'll Need 2-3 Additional Examples 2-3 Test-Taking Strategies 2, with practice sheet	Lesson Quiz 2-3 Student Edition Answers 2-3
Technology	Interactive Textbook Online ExamView Assessment Suite Teacher Express Presentation Express with QuickTake	Worksheets Online Success Tracker Online Intervention

Lesson 2-4

Reasoning in Algebra

INTRODUCE

Check Skills You'll Need (p. 103)
Students review naming angles and rays and finding angle measures.

FACILITATE

Math Background (p. 103)
Discuss with students the three types of properties in mathematics: assumed, defining, and deduced.

Quick Check questions (pp. 104–105)
Assign these questions after each Example to see whether students understand the concepts presented.

Objectives
▼ Connect reasoning in algebra and geometry

New Vocabulary
Reflexive Property, Symmetric Property, Transitive Property

Standards
• NCTM Standards: Algebra, Geometry, Problem Solving, Reasoning and Proof, Communication, Connections, Representation

	Informal Geometry Course	Optional Material
Teaching Guide	▼*Connecting Reasoning in Algebra and Geometry* (pp. 103–105) **Example 1:** Justifying Steps in Solving an Equation **Example 2:** Justifying Steps in Solving an Equation **Example 3:** Using Properties of Equality and Congruence TE: Additional Examples 1–3, page 105	Activity Lab: *Hands-On: Paper-Folding Constructions* (p. 102) *Guided Problem Solving* (p. 109)
Assignment Guide	▼Informal Geometry Exercises: 1–24	▼Exercises: 25–30 Extension: 31–37
Assessment Guide	Test Prep: Exercises 38–42 Mixed Review: Exercises 43–53 TE: Lesson Quiz: 2-4	

RESOURCE OPTIONS

Teaching Resources	Chapter 2 Grab & Go File:
	    Practice 2-4, Reteaching 2-4,
	    Enrichment 2-4
	 Spanish Vocabulary Workbook and Study Skills
		All-in-One Student Workbook 2-4
		 Spanish Practice Workbook

Transparencies	Check Skills You'll Need 2-4 Additional Examples 2-4 Test-Taking Strategies 2, with practice sheet	Lesson Quiz 2-4 Student Edition Answers 2-4
Technology	Interactive Textbook Online ExamView Assessment Suite Teacher Express Presentation Express with QuickTake	Worksheets Online Success Tracker Online Intervention

Lesson 2-5

Proving Angles Congruent

INTRODUCE

Check Skills You'll Need (p. 110)
Students review finding the measures of angles and defining basic geometric terms.
Hands-On Activity (p. 110)
Students use paper folding to discover Thm 2-1.

FACILITATE

Math Background (p. 110)
Remind students that inductive reasoning can lead only to conjectures. However, deductive reasoning can lead to conclusive truths.
Quick Check questions (pp. 111–112)
Assign these after each Example to see whether students understand the concepts presented.

Objectives
▼ Prove and apply theorems about angles

New Vocabulary
theorem, paragraph proof

Standards
• NCTM Standards: Geometry, Problem Solving, Reasoning and Proof, Communication, Connections, Representation

	Informal Geometry Course	Optional Material
Teaching Guide	▼*Theorems About Angles* (pp. 110–112) **Example 1:** Using the Vertical Angles Theorem **Example 2:** Proving Theorem 2-2 TE: Additional Examples 1–2, pages 111–112	Activty Lab: *Hands-On:* Paper-Folding *Comstructions* (p. 102)
Assignment Guide	▼Informal Geometry Exercises: 1–7, 12–13, 16–18, 20	▼Exercises: 8–11, 14, 15, 19, 21–26, 27, 28 Extension: 29–32
Assessment Guide	Test Prep: Exercises 33–39 Mixed Review: Exercises 40–47 TE: Lesson Quiz: 2-5	Chapter Review (pp. 117–119) Chapter Test (p. 120) Stand. Test Prep (p. 121)

RESOURCE OPTIONS

Teaching Resources	Chapter 2 Grab & Go File:
	   Practice 2-5, Reteaching 2-5,
	   Enrichment 2-5
	Alternative Assessment, Form C
	Geometry Test Preparation
	Spanish Vocabulary Workbook and Study Skills
		All-in-One Student Workbook 2-5
		Spanish Practice Workbook
		Hands-On Activities 6
		Chapter 2 Test, Forms F and G

Transparencies	Check Skills You'll Need 2-5 Additional Examples 2-5 Test-Taking Strategies 2, with practice sheet	Lesson Quiz 2-5 Student Edition Answers 2-5
Technology	Interactive Textbook Online ExamView Assessment Suite Teacher Express Presentation Express with QuickTake	Worksheets Online Success Tracker Online Intervention Mindpoint Quiz Show

Lesson 3-1

Properties of Parallel Lines

INTRODUCE

Check Skills You'll Need (p. 127)
Students review writing and solving equations.

FACILITATE

Math Background (p. 127)
Discuss with students the importance of
Euclid's Parallel Postulate (a variation of
the Corresponding Angles Postulate) to the
development of hyperbolic and elliptic geometry.
Quick Check questions (pp. 127–130)
Assign these questions after each Example to see
whether students understand the concepts
presented.

Objectives
▼ Identify angles formed by two lines and a
transversal
▼ Prove and use properties of parallel lines

New Vocabulary
transversal, alternate interior angles, same-side
interior angles, corresponding angles, two-
column proof, alternate exterior angles, same-
side exterior angles.

Standards
• NCTM Standards: Algebra, Geometry,
Measurement, Problem Solving, Reasoning
and Proof, Communication, Connections,
Representation

	Informal Geometry Course	Optional Material
Teaching Guide	▼*Identifying Angles* (pp. 127–128) **Example 1:** Identifying Angles **Example 2:** Real-World Connection ▼*Properties of Parallel Lines* (pp. 128–130) **Example 3:** Writing a Two-Column Proof **Example 4:** Finding Measures of Angles **Example 5:** Using Algebra to Find Angle Measures TE: Additional Examples 1–5, pages 128–130	Activity Lab: *Technology: Parallel Lines and Related Angles* (p. 126)
Assignment Guide	▼Informal Geometry Exercises: 1–8, 19–22, 26, 27 ▼Informal Geometry Exercises: 9–16, 23, 29	▼Extension: 32 ▼Exercises: 17, 18, 24, 25, 28–30 Extension: 31, 33–36
Assessment Guide	Test Prep: Exercises 37–41 Mixed Review: Exercises 42–50 TE: Lesson Quiz: 3-1	

RESOURCE OPTIONS

Teaching Resources	Chapter 3 Grab & Go File:
	  Practice 3-1, Reteaching 3-1,
	  Enrichment 3-1
	Spanish Vocabulary Workbook and Study Skills
		All-in-One Student Workbook 3-1
		Spanish Practice Workbook

Transparencies	Check Skills You'll Need 3-1 Additional Examples 3-1 Test-Taking Strategies 3, with practice sheet	Lesson Quiz 3-1 Student Edition Answers 3-1
Technology	Interactive Textbook Online ExamView Assessment Suite Teacher Express Presentation Express with QuickTake	Worksheets Online Success Tracker Online Intervention

Lesson 3-2

Proving Lines Parallel

INTRODUCE

Check Skills You'll Need (p. 134)
Students practice solving equations and writing
the converse of conditional statements.

FACILITATE

Math Background (p. 134)
Discuss with students Euclid's *The Elements,* and
how the only postulate accepted without proof is
the Corresponding Angles Postulate because its
converse was proved.

Quick Check questions (pp. 135–137)
Assign these questions after each Example to see
whether students understand the concepts
presented.

Objectives
▽ Use a transversal in proving lines parallel

New Vocabulary
flow proof

Standards
• NCTM Standards: Algebra, Geometry,
Problem Solving, Reasoning and Proof,
Communication, Connections,
Representation

	Informal Geometry Course	Optional Material
Teaching Guide	▽ *Using a Transversal* (pp. 122–123) **Example 1:** Using Theorems 3-5 and 3-6 **Example 2:** Using Algebra **Example 3:** Real-World Connection TE: Additional Examples 1–3, pages 135–136	
Assignment Guide	▽ Informal Geometry Exercises: 1–21, 24–26	▽ Exercises: 22–23, 27, 28, 29–40 Extension: 41–45
Assessment Guide	Test Prep: Exercises 46–50 Mixed Review: Exercises 51–65 TE: Lesson Quiz: 3-2	

RESOURCE OPTIONS

Teaching Resources	Chapter 3 Grab & Go File:
	     Practice 3-2, Reteaching 3-2,
	     Enrichment 3-2
	 Spanish Vocabulary Workbook and Study Skills
		All-in-One Student Workbook 3-2
		 Spanish Practice Workbook
		 Hands-On Activities 7

Transparencies	Check Skills You'll Need 3-2 Additional Examples 3-2 Test-Taking Strategies 3, with practice sheet	Lesson Quiz 3-2 Student Edition Answers 3-2
Technology	Interactive Textbook Online ExamView Assessment Suite Teacher Express Presentation Express with QuickTake	Worksheets Online Success Tracker Online Intervention

Lesson 3-3

Parallel and Perpendicular Lines

INTRODUCE

Check Skills You'll Need (p. 141)
Students practice solving equations and writing the converse of conditional statements.

FACILITATE

Math Background (p. 141)
Discuss with students Euclid's *The Elements*, and how the only postulate accepted without proof is the Corresponding Angles Postulate because its converse was proved.

Quick Check questions (p. 142)
Assign these questions after each Example to see whether students understand the concepts presented.

Objectives
▼ Relate parallel and perpendicular lines

New Vocabulary
none

Standards
• NCTM Standards: Algebra, Geometry, Problem Solving, Reasoning and Proof, Communication, Connections, Representation

	Informal Geometry Course	Optional Material
Teaching Guide	▼*Relating Parallel and Perpendicular Lines* (pp. 141–142) **Example 1:** Real-World Connection **Example 2:** Using Theorem 3-11 TE: Additional Examples 1–2, page 142	*Guided Problem Solving* (p. 145)
Assignment Guide	▼Informal Geometry Exercises: 1–2, 4–10	▼Exercises: 3, 11–13, Extension: 14–23
Assessment Guide	Test Prep: Exercises 24–25 Mixed Review: Exercises 26–29 TE: Lesson Quiz: 3-3	

RESOURCE OPTIONS

Teaching Resources	Chapter 3 Grab & Go File:
	  Practice 3-3, Reteaching 3-3,
	  Enrichment 3-3
	Technology Activities 40
	Spanish Vocabulary Workbook and Study Skills
		All-in-One Student Workbook 3-3
		Spanish Practice Workbook
		Hands-On Activities 8

Transparencies	Check Skills You'll Need 3-3 Additional Examples 3-3 Test-Taking Strategies 3, with practice sheet	Lesson Quiz 3-3 Student Edition Answers 3-3
Technology	Interactive Textbook Online ExamView Assessment Suite Teacher Express Presentation Express with QuickTake	Worksheets Online Success Tracker Online Intervention

Lesson 3-4

Parallel Lines and the Triangle Angle-Sum Theorem

INTRODUCE

Check Skills You'll Need (p. 147)
Students review classifying angles and solving equations.

Activity Lab (p. 146)
Students draw a triangle, tear off each angle, and then place the angles together to discover the sum of the measures of a triangle.

FACILITATE

Math Background (p. 147)
Discuss with students how the Triangle Angle-Sum Theorem is only true in Euclidean geometry.

Quick Check questions (pp. 148–150)
Assign these after each Example to see whether students understand the concepts presented.

Objectives
▼ Classify triangles and find the measures of their angles
▼ Use exterior angles of triangles

New Vocabulary
acute triangle, right triangle, obtuse triangle, equiangular triangle, equilateral triangle, isosceles triangle, scalene triangle, exterior angle of a polygon, remote interior angles

Standards
* NCTM Standards: Algebra, Geometry, Measurement, Problem Solving, Reasoning and Proof, Communication, Connections, Representation

	Informal Geometry Course	Optional Material
Teaching Guide	▼ *Finding Angle Measures in Triangles* (pp. 146–148) **Example 1:** Applying the Triangle Angle-Sum Theorem **Example 2:** Using Algebra **Example 3:** Classifying a Triangle ▼ *Using Exterior Angles of Triangles* (pp. 149–150) **Example 4:** Using the Exterior Angle Theorem **Example 5:** Real-World Connection TE: Additional Examples 1–5, pages 148–149	Activity Lab: *Angle Dynamics* (p. 146) Activity Lab: *Exploring Spherical Geometry* (pp. 154–155)
Assignment Guide	▼ Informal Geometry Exercises: 1–15, 23–24 ▼ Informal Geometry Exercises: 16–22	▼ Exercises: 25, 27–32, 34, ▼ Exercises: 26, 33, 35, 36 Extension: 37, 38–41
Assessment Guide	Test Prep: Exercises 42–44 Mixed Review: Exercises 45–49 Checkpoint Quiz 1; TE: Lesson Quiz: 3-4	

RESOURCE OPTIONS

Teaching Resources	Chapter 3 Grab & Go File:
	    Practice 3-4, Reteaching 3-4,
	    Enrichment 3-4
	 Technology Activities 40
	 Spanish Vocabulary Workbook and Study Skills
		All-in-One Student Workbook 3-4
		 Spanish Practice Workbook
		 Hands-On Activities 8

Transparencies	Check Skills You'll Need 3-4 Additional Examples 3-4 Test-Taking Strategies 3, with practice sheet	Lesson Quiz 3-4 Student Edition Answers 3-4
Technology	Interactive Textbook Online ExamView Assessment Suite Teacher Express Presentation Express with QuickTake	Worksheets Online Success Tracker Online Intervention

Lesson 3-5

The Polygon Angle-Sum Theorems

INTRODUCE

Check Skills You'll Need (p. 157)
Students review finding angle measures of given quadrilaterals.
Activity (p. 159)
Students draw triangles in polygons to begin to discover the Polygon Angle-Sum Theorem.

FACILITATE

Math Background (p. 157)
Discuss with students how number theory allows them to determine whether a regular polygon will tessellate a plane.
Quick Check questions (pp. 157–160)
Assign these questions after each Example to see whether students understand the concepts presented.

Objectives
▼ Classify polygons
▼ Find the sums of the measures of the interior and exterior angles of polygons

New Vocabulary
polygon, convex polygon, concave polygon, equilateral polygon, equiangular polygon, regular polygon

Standards
• NCTM Standards: Algebra, Geometry, Problem Solving, Reasoning and Proof, Communication, Connections, Representation

	Informal Geometry Course	**Optional Material**
Teaching Guide	▼ *Classifying Polygons* (pp. 157–158) **Example 1:** Naming Polygons **Example 2:** Real-World Connection ▼ *Polygon Angle Sums* (pp. 159–160) **Example 3:** Finding a Polygon Angle Sum **Example 4:** Using the Polygon Angle-Sum Theorem **Example 5:** Real-World Connection TE: Additional Examples 1–5, pages 159–160	Activity Lab: *Technology: Exploring the Exterior Angles of a Polygon* (p. 156)
Assignment Guide	▼ Informal Geometry Exercises: 1–10 ▼ Informal Geometry Exercises: 11–35, 36	▼ Exercises: 50–53 Extension: 60–63 ▼ Exercises: 37–49, 54–56 Extension: 57–59
Assessment Guide	Test Prep: Exercises 64–70 Mixed Review: Exercises 71–86 TE: Lesson Quiz: 3-5	

RESOURCE OPTIONS

Teaching Resources	Chapter 3 Grab & Go File:
	    Practice 3-5, Reteaching 3-5,
	    Enrichment 3-5
	Spanish Vocabulary Workbook and Study Skills
		All-in-One Student Workbook 3-5
		Spanish Practice Workbook
		Hands-On Activities 9

Transparencies	Check Skills You'll Need 3-5 Additional Examples 3-5 Classroom Aid, *Geometric Shapes I* Test-Taking Strategies 3, with practice sheet	Lesson Quiz 3-5 Student Edition Answers 3-5
Technology	Interactive Textbook Online ExamView Assessment Suite Teacher Express Presentation Express with QuickTake	Worksheets Online Success Tracker Online Intervention

Lesson 3-6

Lines in the Coordinate Plane

INTRODUCE

Check Skills You'll Need (p. 166)
Students review finding slope when given two points and graphing a line when given two points.

FACILITATE

Math Background (p. 166)
Discuss with students how a publication by René Descartes eventually led to the invention of calculus.

Quick Check questions (pp. 166–168)
Assign these questions after each Example to see whether students understand the concepts presented.

<table>
<tr><td colspan="2">

Objectives
▼ Graph lines given their equations
▼ Write equations of lines

New Vocabulary
slope-intercept form, standard form of a linear equation, point-slope form

Standards
• NCTM Standards: Algebra, Geometry, Problem Solving, Communication, Connections, Representation
</td></tr>
</table>

	Informal Geometry Course	Optional Material
Teaching Guide	▼ *Graphing Lines* (pp. 166–167) **Example 1:** Graphing Lines in Slope-Intercept Form **Example 2:** Graphing Lines Using Intercepts **Example 3:** Transforming to Slope-Intercept Form ▼ *Writing Equations of Lines* (p. 168) **Example 4:** Using Point-Slope Form **Example 5:** Writing an Equation of a Line Given Two Points **Example 6:** Equations of Horizontal and Vertical Lines TE: Additional Examples 1–6, pages 167–168	*Algebra 1 Review: Slope* (p. 165) Activity Lab: *Technology: Solving Linear Equations with Graphs and Tables* (pp. 172–173)
Assignment Guide	▼ Informal Geometry Exercises: 1–16, 33–37, ▼ Informal Geometry Exercises: 17–32, 39–44, 48–51	▼ Exercises: 38, 45–46, 53 Extension: 57–60 ▼ Exercises: 47, 52, 54–56 Extension: 61–63
Assessment Guide	Test Prep: Exercises 64–69 Mixed Review: Exercises 70–80 TE: Lesson Quiz: 3-6	

RESOURCE OPTIONS

Teaching Resources	Chapter 3 Grab & Go File: 　　Practice 3-6, Reteaching 3-6, 　　Enrichment 3-6 Spanish Vocabulary Workbook and Study Skills	All-in-One Student Workbook 3-6 Spanish Practice Workbook
Transparencies	Check Skills You'll Need 3-6 Additional Examples 3-6 Classroom Aid: *Coordinate Plane, Slope of a Line, Equations of a Line,* and *Graphing Calculator Grid* Test-Taking Strategies 3, with practice sheet	Lesson Quiz 3-6 Student Edition Answers 3-6
Technology	Interactive Textbook Online ExamView Assessment Suite Teacher Express Presentation Express with QuickTake	Worksheets Online Success Tracker Online Intervention

Lesson 3-7

···

Slopes of Parallel and Perpendicular Lines

NTRODUCE

Check Skills You'll Need (p. 174)
Students review finding slope when given two
points and when given an equation of a line.

FACILITATE

Math Background (p. 174)
Discuss with students how the product of the
slopes of perpendicular lines is an application of
the Pythagorean Theorem.
Quick Check questions (pp. 174–177)
Assign these after each Example to see whether
students understand the concepts presented.

Objectives
▼ Relate slope and parallel lines
▼ Relate slope and perpendicular lines

New Vocabulary
none

Standards
• NCTM Standards: Algebra, Geometry,
Problem Solving, Communication,
Connections, Representation

	Informal Geometry Course	Optional Material
Teaching Guide	▼*Slope and Parallel Lines* (pp. 174–175) **Example 1:** Checking for Parallel Lines **Example 2:** Determining Whether Lines are Parallel **Example 3:** Writing Equations of Parallel Lines ▼*Slope and Perpendicular Lines* (pp. 175–177) **Example 4:** Checking for Perpendicular Lines **Example 5:** Writing Equations for Perpendicular Lines **Example 6:** Real-World Connection TE: Additional Examples 1–6, pages 175–176	
Assignment Guide	▼Informal Geometry Exercises: 1–15 ▼Informal Geometry Exercises: 16–24, 26–27	▼Exercises: 29–32, 34, 35, 37 Extension: 47 ▼Exercises: 25, 28, 33, 36, 38–44 Extension: 45, 46, 48
Assessment Guide	Test Prep: Exercises 49–52 Mixed Review: Exercises 53–61 Checkpoint Quiz 2	

RESOURCE OPTIONS

Teaching Resources	Chapter 3 Grab & Go File:
	  Practice 3-7, Reteaching 3-7,
	  Enrichment 3-7
	Spanish Vocabulary Workbook and Study Skills
		All-in-One Student Workbook 3-7
		Spanish Practice Workbook

Transparencies	Check Skills You'll Need 3-7 Additional Examples 3-7 Test-Taking Strategies 3, with practice sheet	Lesson Quiz 3-7 Student Edition Answers 3-7
Technology	Interactive Textbook Online ExamView Assessment Suite Teacher Express Presentation Express with QuickTake	Worksheets Online Success Tracker Online Intervention

···

Lesson 3-8

Constructing Parallel and Perpendicular Lines

NTRODUCE

Check Skills You'll Need (p. 181)
Students review using a straightedge and compass for basic constructions.

FACILITATE

Math Background (p. 181)
Discuss with students variations in constructing parallel and perpendicular lines.

Quick Check questions (pp. 181–183)
Assign these questions after each Example to see whether students understand the concepts presented.

> **Objectives**
> ▼ Construct parallel lines
> ▼ Construct perpendicular lines
>
> **New Vocabulary**
> none
>
> **Standards**
> • NCTM Standards: Geometry, Problem Solving, Communication, Connections, Representation

	Informal Geometry Course	Optional Material
Teaching Guide	▼ *Constructing Parallel Lines* (pp. 181–182) **Example 1:** Constructing $\ell \parallel m$ **Example 2:** Constructing a Special Quadrilateral ▼ *Constructing Perpendicular Lines* (pp. 182–183) **Example 3:** Perpendicular at a Point on a Line **Example 4:** Perpendicular From a Point to a Line TE: Additional Examples 1–4, pages 182–183	Activity Lab: *Technology: Using Tables and Lists* (p. 187)
Assignment Guide	▼ Informal Geometry Exercises: 1–7, 16 ▼ Informal Geometry Exercises: 8–13, 17	▼ Exercises: 14, 15, Extension: 27, 33–36 ▼ Exercises: 18–26, Extension: 28–32
Assessment Guide	Test Prep: Exercises 37–40 Mixed Review: Exercises 41–47 TE: Lesson Quiz: 3-8	Chapter Review (pp. 189–191) Chapter Test (p. 192) Stand. Test Prep (p. 193)

RESOURCE OPTIONS

Teaching Resources	Chapter 3 Grab & Go File: 　Practice 3-8, Reteaching 3-8, 　Enrichment 3-8 Chapter 3 Test, Forms F and G Geometry Test Preparation Spanish Vocabulary Workbook and Study Skills	All-in-One Student Workbook 3-8 Spanish Practice Workbook Alternative Assessment, Form C Quarter 1 Test, Forms D and E
Transparencies	Check Skills You'll Need 3-8 Additional Examples 3-8 Test-Taking Strategies 3, with practice sheet	Lesson Quiz 3-8 Student Edition Answers 3-8
Technology	Interactive Textbook Online ExamView Assessment Suite Teacher Express Presentation Express with QuickTake	Worksheets Online Success Tracker Online Intervention Mindpoint Quiz Show

Lesson 4-1

Congruent Figures

INTRODUCE

Check Skills You'll Need (p. 198)
Students practice solving equations and using the Triangle Angle-Sum Theorem.

FACILITATE

Math Background (p. 198)
Remind students of the one-to-one correspondence between corresponding parts of congruent polygons.

Quick Check questions (pp. 198–200)
Assign these questions after each Example to see whether students understand the concepts presented.

Objectives
▼ Recognize congruent figures and their corresponding parts

New Vocabulary
congruent polygons

Standards
• NCTM Standards: Geometry, Problem Solving, Reasoning and Proof, Communication, Connections, Representation

	Informal Geometry Course	**Optional Material**
Teaching Guide	▼ *Congruent Figures* (pp. 198–200) **Example 1:** Naming Congruent Parts **Example 2:** Real-World Connection **Example 3:** Finding Congruent Triangles **Example 4:** Proving Triangles Congruent TE: Additional Examples 1–4, page 200	
Assignment Guide	▼ Informal Geometry Exercises 1–29, 34–36	▼ Exercises: 30–33, 37–45 Extension: 46–48
Assessment Guide	Test Prep: Exercises 49–52 Mixed Review: Exercises 53–59 TE: Lesson Quiz: 4-1	

RESOURCE OPTIONS

Teaching Resources	Chapter 4 Grab & Go File:
	    Practice 4-1, Reteaching 4-1
	    Enrichment 4-1
	 Spanish Vocabulary Workbook and Study Guide
		All-in-One Student Workbook 4-1
		 Spanish Practice Workbook 4-1
		 Hands-On Activities 10

Transparencies	Check Skills You'll Need 4-1 Additional Examples 4-1 Test-Taking Strategies 4, with practice sheet	Lesson Quiz 4-1 Student Edition Answers 4-1
Technology	Interactive Textbook Online ExamView Assessment Suite Teacher Express Presentation Express with QuickTake	Worksheets Online Success Tracker Online Intervention

Lesson 4-2

Triangle Congruence by SSS and SAS

INTRODUCE

Check Skills You'll Need (p. 205)
Students review identifying congruent angles, congruent sides, and parallel sides of triangles.

Activity Lab (p. 204)
Students use straws to form and compare triangles with sides of a given length to begin their discovery of the SSS Postulate.

FACILITATE

Math Background (p. 205)
Remind students that only four congruence statements (SSS, SAS, ASA, or AAS) are needed to prove two triangles congruent, even though there are six possible congruences.

Quick Check questions (pp. 206–207) Assign these questions after each Example to see whether students understand the concepts presented.

Objectives
▼ Prove two triangles congruent using the SSS and SAS Postulates

New Vocabulary
none

Standards
- NCTM Standards: Geometry, Problem Solving, Reasoning and Proof, Communication, Connections, Representation

---

	Informal Geometry Course	**Optional Material**
Teaching Guide	▼ *Using the SSS and SAS Postulates* (pp. 205–207) **Example 1:** Using SSS **Example 2:** Using SAS **Example 3:** Are the Triangles Congruent? TE: Additional Examples 1–3, page 207	Activity Lab: *Hands-On: Building Congruent Triangles* (p. 204)
Assignment Guide	▼ Informal Geometry Exercises: 1–27	▼ Exercises: 28–39 Extension: 40–43
Assessment Guide	Test Prep: Exercises 44–47 Mixed Review: Exercises 48–55 TE: Lesson Quiz: 4-2	

RESOURCE OPTIONS

Teaching Resources	Chapter 4 Grab & Go File: Practice 4-2, Reteaching 4-2 Enrichment 4-2 Spanish Vocabulary Workbook and Study Guide	All-in-One Student Workbook 4-2 Spanish Practice Workbook 4-2 Hands-On Activities 11
Transparencies	Check Skills You'll Need 4-2 Additional Examples 4-2 Test-Taking Strategies 4, with practice sheet	Lesson Quiz 4-2 Student Edition Answers 4-2
Technology	Interactive Textbook Online ExamView Assessment Suite Teacher Express Presentation Express with QuickTake	Worksheets Online Success Tracker Online Intervention

Lesson 4-3

Triangle Congruence by ASA and AAS

INTRODUCE

Check Skills You'll Need (p. 213)
Students review included angles and included sides, and congruence properties.

Activity Lab (p. 220)
Students use constructions to create congruent triangles that lead to a discovery of the ASA Postulate.

FACILITATE

Math Background (p. 213)
Discuss with students how both the ASA Postulate and the SSS Postulate could be established as theorems derived from the SAS Postulate.

Quick Check questions (pp. 213–215)
Assign these questions after each Example to see whether students understand the concepts presented.

Objectives
▼ Prove triangles congruent using the ASA Postulate and the AAS Theorem

New Vocabulary
none

Standards
• NCTM Standards: Geometry, Problem Solving, Reasoning and Proof, Communication, Connections, Representation

	Informal Geometry Course	Optional Material
Teaching Guide	▼ *Using the ASA Postulate and the AAS Theorem* (pp. 213–215) **Example 1:** Using ASA **Example 2:** Real-World Connection **Example 3:** Planning a Proof **Example 4:** Writing a Proof TE: Additional Examples 1–4, pages 214–215	Activity Lab: *Technology: Exploring AAA and SSA* (p. 220)
Assignment Guide	▼ Informal Geometry Exercises: 1–16	▼ Exercises: 17–26 Extension: 27–32
Assessment Guide	Test Prep: Exercises 33–36 Mixed Review: Exercises 37–43 Checkpoint Quiz 1 TE: Lesson Quiz: 4-3	

RESOURCE OPTIONS

Teaching Resources	Chapter 4 Grab & Go File:
	    Practice 4-3, Reteaching 4-3
	    Enrichment 4-3
	 Spanish Vocabulary Workbook and Study Guide
		All-in-One Student Workbook 4-3
		 Spanish Practice Workbook 4-3
		 Technology Activities 41

Transparencies	Check Skills You'll Need 4-3 Additional Examples 4-3 Test-Taking Strategies 4, with practice sheet	Lesson Quiz 4-3 Student Edition Answers 4-3
Technology	Interactive Textbook Online ExamView Assessment Suite Teacher Express Presentation Express with QuickTake	Worksheets Online Success Tracker Online Intervention

Lesson 4-4

Using Congruent Triangles: CPCTC

INTRODUCE

Check Skills You'll Need (p. 221)
Students review identifying congruent corresponding angles and sides.

FACILITATE

Math Background (p. 221)
Explain to students the benefit of using CPCTC when proving congruence statements among polygons.

Quick Check questions (pp. 221–222)
Assign these questions after each Example to see whether students understand the concepts presented.

Objectives
▼ Use triangle congruence and CPCTC to prove that parts of two triangles are congruent

New Vocabulary
CPCTC

Standards
• NCTM Standards: Geometry, Problem Solving, Reasoning and Proof, Communication, Connections, Representation

	Informal Geometry Course	**Optional Material**
Teaching Guide	▼*Proving Parts of Triangles Congruent* (pp. 221–222) **Example 1:** Real-World Connection **Example 2:** Real-World Connection TE: Additional Examples 1 and 2, page 222	*Guided Problem Solving* (p. 226)
Assignment Guide	▼Informal Geometry Exercises: 1–11	▼Exercises: 12–19 Extension: 20, 21
Assessment Guide	Test Prep: Exercises 22–25 Mixed Review: Exercises 26–31 TE: Lesson Quiz: 4-4	

RESOURCE OPTIONS

Teaching Resources	Chapter 4 Grab & Go File: Practice 4-4, Reteaching 4-4 Enrichment 4-4 Spanish Vocabulary Workbook and Study Guide	All-in-One Student Workbook 4-4 Spanish Practice Workbook 4-4
Transparencies	Check Skills You'll Need 4-4 Additional Examples 4-4 Test-Taking Strategies 4, with practice sheet	Lesson Quiz 4-4 Student Edition Answers 4-4
Technology	Interactive Textbook Online ExamView Assessment Suite Teacher Express Presentation Express with QuickTake	Worksheets Online Success Tracker Online Intervention

Lesson 4-5

···
Isosceles and Equilateral Triangles

INTRODUCE

Check Skills You'll Need (p. 228)
Students review identifying angles opposite a given side and sides opposite a given angle.
Activity Lab (p. 227)
Students construct an isosceles triangle, and by manipulating the triangle they discover Theorem 4-3.

FACILITATE

Math Background (p. 228)
Discuss with students how root words often give clues to the meanings of mathematical terms.
Quick Check questions (pp. 229–230)
Assign these questions after each Example to see whether students understand the concepts presented.

Objectives
▼ Use and apply properties of isosceles triangles

New Vocabulary
legs of an isosceles triangle, base of an isosceles triangle, vertex angle of an isosceles triangle, base angles of an isosceles triangle, corollary

Standards
• NCTM Standards: Algebra, Geometry, Problem Solving, Reasoning and Proof, Communication, Connections, Representation

---

	Informal Geometry Course	Optional Material
Teaching Guide	▼ *The Isosceles Triangle Theorems* (pp. 228–230) **Example 1:** Using the Isosceles Triangle Theorems **Example 2:** Using Algebra **Example 3:** Real-World Connection TE: Additional Examples 1–3, page 230	Activity Lab: *Hands-On: Paper-Folding Conjecture* (p. 227) *Algebra 1 Review: Systems of Linear Equations* (p. 234)
Assignment Guide	▼ Informal Geometry Exercises: 1–20	▼ Exercises: 20–32 Extension: 33–40
Assessment Guide	Test Prep: Exercises 41–44 Mixed Review: Exercises 45–48 TE: Lesson Quiz: 4-5	

RESOURCE OPTIONS

Teaching Resources	Chapter 4 Grab & Go File: Practice 4-5, Reteaching 4-5 Enrichment 4-5 Spanish Vocabulary Workbook and Study Guide	All-in-One Student Workbook 4-5 Spanish Practice Workbook 4-5
Transparencies	Check Skills You'll Need 4-5 Additional Examples 4-5 Test-Taking Strategies 4, with practice sheet	Lesson Quiz 4-5 Student Edition Answers 4-5
Technology	Interactive Textbook Online ExamView Assessment Suite Teacher Express Presentation Express with QuickTake	Worksheets Online Success Tracker Online Intervention

···

Lesson 4-6

Congruence in Right Triangles

INTRODUCE

Check Skills You'll Need (p. 235)
Students review the triangle congruence theorems and postulates from previous lessons of the chapter.

FACILITATE

Math Background (p. 235)
Discuss with students how the HL Theorem is an example of the SSA or the SSS relationship.
Quick Check questions (pp. 236–237)
Assign these questions after each Example to see whether students understand the concepts presented.

Objectives
▼ Prove triangles congruent using the HL Theorem

New Vocabulary
hypotenuse, legs of a right triangle

Standards
• NCTM Standards: Geometry, Problem Solving, Reasoning and Proof, Communication, Connections, Representation

	Informal Geometry Course	Optional Material
Teaching Guide	▼ *The Hypotenuse-Leg Theorem* (pp. 235–237) **Example 1:** Real-World Connection **Example 2:** Using the HL Theorem **Example 3:** Using the HL Theorem TE: Additional Examples 1–3, page 237	
Assignment Guide	▼Informal Geometry Exercises: 1–15	▼Exercises: 16–24 Extension: 25, 26
Assessment Guide	Test Prep: Exercises 27–30 Mixed Review: Exercises 31–39 Checkpoint Quiz 2 TE: Lesson Quiz: 4-6	

RESOURCE OPTIONS

Teaching Resources	Chapter 4 Grab & Go File:
	    Practice 4-6, Reteaching 4-6
	    Enrichment 4-6
	 Geometry Test Preparation
	 Spanish Vocabulary Workbook and Study Guide
		All-in-One Student Workbook 4-6
		 Spanish Practice Workbook 4-6
		 Alternative Assessment, Form C

Transparencies	Check Skills You'll Need 4-6 Additional Examples 4-6 Test-Taking Strategies 4, with practice sheet	Lesson Quiz 4-6 Student Edition Answers 4-6
Technology	Interactive Textbook Online ExamView Assessment Suite Teacher Express Presentation Express with QuickTake	Worksheets Online Success Tracker Online Intervention

Lesson 4-7

Using Corresponding Parts of Congruent Triangles

ABOUT THIS LESSON

This lesson is not typically needed in an Informal Geometry Course. Check your state guidelines to see whether you should cover any of the Optional Material listed below.

Objectives
▼ Identify congruent overlapping triangles
▼ Prove two triangles congruent by first proving two other triangles congruent

New Vocabulary
none

Standards
• NCTM Standards: Geometry, Problem Solving, Reasoning and Proof, Communication, Connections, Representation

	Informal Geometry Course	Optional Material
Teaching Guide		▼ *Using Overlapping Triangles in Proofs* (pp. 241–242) **Example 1:** Identifying Common Parts **Example 2:** Using Common Parts ▼ *Using Two Pairs of Congruent Triangles* (pp. 242–243) **Example 3:** Using Two Pairs of Triangles **Example 4:** Separating Overlapping Triangles TE: Additional Examples 1–4, pages 242–243 *Extension: Writing Flow Proofs* (p. 247)
Assignment Guide		▼ Exercises: 1–9, 12–15; Extension: 23 ▼ Exercises: 10–11, 16–22; Extension: 24, 25
Assessment Guide	Mixed Review: Exercises 31–40	Test Prep: Exercises 26–30 TE: Lesson Quiz: 4-7 Chapter Review (pp. 249–251) Chapter Test (p. 252) Standardized Test Prep (p. 253)

RESOURCE OPTIONS

Teaching Resources	Chapter 4 Grab & Go File:
	    Practice 4-7, Reteaching 4-7
	    Enrichment 4-7
	 Chapter 4 Test, Forms F and G
	 Spanish Vocabulary Workbook and Study Skills
		All-in-One Student Workbook 4-7
		 Spanish Practice Workbook 4-7
		 Alternative Assessment, Form C
		 Geometry Test Preparation

Transparencies	Check Skills You'll Need 4-7 Additional Examples 4-7 Test-Taking Strategies 4, with practice sheet	Lesson Quiz 4-7 Student Edition Answers 4-7
Technology	Interactive Textbook Online ExamView Assessment Suite Teacher Express Presentation Express with QuickTake	Worksheets Online Success Tracker Online Intervention Mindpoint Quiz Show

Lesson 5-1

Midsegments of Triangles

INTRODUCE

Check Skills You'll Need (p. 259)
Students review finding the slope and midpoint of two given points.

Hands-On Activity (p. 259)
Students draw, cut out, and manipulate triangles through paper folding to discover Theorem 5-1.

FACILITATE

Math Background (p. 259)
Discuss with students that the Triangle Midsegment Theorem can be proved without using coordinate geometry.

Quick Check questions (pp. 260–261)
Assign these questions after each Example to see whether students understand the concepts presented.

Objectives
▼ Use properties of midsegments to solve problems

New Vocabulary
midsegment, coordinate proof

Standards
• NCTM Standards: Number and Operations, Algebra, Geometry, Measurement, Problem Solving, Reasoning and Proof, Communication, Connections, Representation

	Informal Geometry Course	Optional Material
Teaching Guide	▼ *Using Properties of Midsegments* (pp. 259–261) **Example 1:** Finding Lengths **Example 2:** Identifying Parallel Segments **Example 3:** Real-World Connection TE: Additional Examples 1–3, page 261	*Technology: Investigating Midsegments* (p. 258)
Assignment Guide	▼ Informal Geometry Exercises: 1–20, 22, 26, 27	▼ Exercises: 21, 23–25, 28–33 Extension: 34–36
Assessment Guide	Test Prep: Exercises 37–43 Mixed Review: Exercises 44–52 TE: Lesson Quiz: 5-1	

RESOURCE OPTIONS

Teaching Resources	Chapter 5 Grab & Go File: Practice 5-1, Reteaching 5-1 Enrichment 5-1 Spanish Vocabulary Workbook and Study Skills	All-in-One Student Workbook 5-1 Spanish Practice Workbook 5-1
Transparencies	Check Skills You'll Need 5-1 Additional Examples 5-1 Test-Taking Strategies 5, with practice sheet	Lesson Quiz 5-1 Student Edition Answers 5-1
Technology	Interactive Textbook Online ExamView Assessment Suite Teacher Express Presentation Express with QuickTake	Worksheets Online Success Tracker Online Intervention

Lesson 5-2

• •

Bisectors in Triangles

INTRODUCE

Check Skills You'll Need (p. 265)
Students review constructing congruent triangles, congruent angles, a perpendicular bisector, and an angle bisector.

FACILITATE

Math Background (p. 265)
Explain to students that a perpendicular bisector and angle bisector can be described using locus theorems.

Quick Check questions (pp. 266–267)
Assign these questions after each Example to see whether students understand the concepts presented.

Objectives
▼ Use properties of perpendicular bisectors and angle bisectors

New Vocabulary
distance from a point to a line

Standards
• NCTM Standards: Geometry, Problem Solving, Reasoning and Proof, Communication, Connections, Representation

	Informal Geometry Course	**Optional Material**
Teaching Guide	▼ *Perpendicular Bisectors and Angle Bisectors* (pp. 265–267) **Example 1:** Real-World Connection **Example 2:** Using the Angle Bisector Theorem TE: Additional Examples 1 and 2, page 266	
Assignment Guide	▼ Informal Geometry Exercises: 1–16, 18–26	▼ Exercises: 17, 27–48 Extension: 49, 50
Assessment Guide	Test Prep: Exercises 51–55 Mixed Review: Exercises 56–67 TE: Lesson Quiz: 5-2	

RESOURCE OPTIONS

Teaching Resources	Chapter 5 Grab & Go File: Practice 5-2, Reteaching 5-2 Enrichment 5-2 Spanish Vocabulary Workbook and Study Skills	All-in-One Student Workbook 5-2 Spanish Practice Workbook 5-2 Hands-On Activities 13
Transparencies	Check Skills You'll Need 5-2 Additional Examples 5-2 Test-Taking Strategies 5, with practice sheet	Lesson Quiz 5-2 Student Edition Answers 5-2
Technology	Interactive Textbook Online ExamView Assessment Suite Teacher Express Presentation Express with QuickTake	Worksheets Online Success Tracker Online Intervention

Lesson 5-3

··

Concurrent Lines, Medians, and Altitudes

INTRODUCE

Check Skills You'll Need (p. 272)
Students review constructing bisectors of angles and segments.

Hands-On Activity (p. 272)
Students draw, cut out, and manipulate triangles through paper folding to discover Theorem 5-6 and Theorem 5-7.

FACILITATE

Math Background (p. 272)
Discuss with students the similarity of the theorems in this lesson to Ceva's Theorem published in 1678.

Quick Check questions (pp. 273–275)
Assign these questions after each Example to see whether students understand the concepts presented.

Objectives
▼ Identify properties of perpendicular bisectors and angle bisectors
▼ Identify properties of medians and altitudes of a triangle

New Vocabulary
concurrent, point of concurrency, circumcenter of a triangle, circumscribed about, incenter of a triangle, inscribed in, median of a triangle, centroid, altitude of a triangle, orthocenter of a triangle

Standards
• NCTM Standards: Geometry, Measurement, Problem Solving, Communication, Connections, Representation

	Informal Geometry Course	Optional Material
Teaching Guide	▼ *Properties of Bisectors* (pp. 272–274) **Example 1:** Finding the Circumcenter **Example 2:** Real-World Connection ▼ *Medians and Altitudes* (pp. 274–275) **Example 3:** Finding Lengths of Medians **Example 4:** Identifying Medians and Altitudes TE: Additional Examples 1–4, pages 273–275	Activity Lab: *Technology: Exploring Special Segments in Triangles* (p. 271)
Assignment Guide	▼ Informal Geometry Exercises: 1–10, 17–19 ▼ Informal Geometry Exercises: 11–16, 20, 22, 25–26	▼ Exercises: 21, 24, 29–31 ▼ Exercises: 23, 27–28, 32 Extension: 33–36
Assessment Guide	Test Prep: Exercises 37–41 Mixed Review: Exercises 42–51 Checkpoint Quiz 1 TE: Lesson Quiz: 5-3	

RESOURCE OPTIONS

Teaching Resources	Chapter 5 Grab & Go File:
	    Practice 5-3, Reteaching 5-3
	    Enrichment 5-3
	Technology Activities 43
	Spanish Vocabulary Workbook and Study Skills
		All-in-One Student Workbook 5-3
		Spanish Practice Workbook 5-3
		Hands-On Activities 14

Transparencies	Check Skills You'll Need 5-3 Additional Examples 5-3 Test-Taking Strategies 5, with practice sheet	Lesson Quiz 5-3 Student Edition Answers 5-3
Technology	Interactive Textbook Online ExamView Assessment Suite Teacher Express Presentation Express with QuickTake	Worksheets Online Success Tracker Online Intervention

All rights reserved.

© Pearson Education, Inc., publishing as Pearson Prentice Hall.

32 Lesson 5-3

Informal Geometry Lesson Plans and Assessments

Lesson 5-4
Inverses, Contrapositives, and Indirect Reasoning

ABOUT THIS LESSON
This lesson is not typically needed in an Informal Geometry Course. Check your state guidelines to see whether you should cover any of the Optional Material listed below.

Objectives
▼ Write the negation of a statement and the inverse and contrapositive of a conditional statement
▼ Use indirect reasoning

New Vocabulary
negation, inverse, contrapositive, equivalent statements, indirect reasoning, indirect proof

Standards
• NCTM Standards: Number and Operations, Geometry, Problem Solving, Reasoning and Proof, Communication, Connections, Representation

	Informal Geometry Course	Optional Material
Teaching Guide		▼*Writing the Negation, Inverse, and Contrapositive* (pp. 280–281) **Example 1:** Writing the Negation of a Statement **Example 2:** Writing the Inverse and Contrapositive ▼*Using Indirect Reasoning* (pp. 281–283) **Example 3:** The First Step of an Indirect Proof **Example 4:** Identifying Contradictions **Example 5:** Indirect Proof TE: Additional Examples 1–5, pages 281–282 *Guided Problem Solving* (p. 287)
Assignment Guide		▼Exercises: 1–9, 22–28, 32–34 ▼Exercises: 10–21, 29–31, 35–40 Extension: 41
Assessment Guide	Mixed Review: Exercises 47–55	Test Prep: Exercises 42–46 TE: Lesson Quiz: 5-4

RESOURCE OPTIONS

Teaching Resources	Chapter 5 Grab & Go File:
	   Practice 5-4, Reteaching 5-4
	   Enrichment 5-4
		All-in-One Student Workbook 5-4
		Spanish Practice Workbook 5-4

	Spanish Vocabulary Workbook and Study Skills	
Transparencies	Check Skills You'll Need 5-4 Additional Examples 5-4 Test-Taking Strategies 5, with practice sheet	Lesson Quiz 5-4 Student Edition Answers 5-4
Technology	Interactive Textbook Online ExamView Assessment Suite Teacher Express Presentation Express with QuickTake	Worksheets Online Success Tracker Online Intervention

Lesson 5-5

Inequalities in Triangles

INTRODUCE

Check Skills You'll Need (p. 289)
Students review graphing triangles, ordering lengths of the sides of a triangle, and the steps of an indirect proof.

FACILITATE

Math Background (p. 289)
Explain to students that Theorems 5-10 and 5-11 can be viewed as extensions of the Isosceles Triangle Theorem and its converse.

Quick Check questions (pp. 290–292)
Assign these after each Example to see whether students understand the concepts presented.

Objectives
▼ Use inequalities involving angles of triangles
▼ Use inequalities involving sides of triangles

New Vocabulary
none

Standards
• NCTM Standards: Algebra, Geometry, Problem Solving, Reasoning and Proof, Communication, Connections, Representation

	Informal Geometry Course	Optional Material
Teaching Guide	▼ *Inequalities Involving Angles of Triangles* (pp. 289–290) **Example 1:** Applying the Corollary **Example 2:** Real-World Connection ▼ *Inequalities Involving Sides of Triangles* (pp. 290–291) **Example 3:** Using Theorem 5-11 **Example 4:** Using the Triangle Inequality Theorem **Example 5:** Finding Possible Side Lengths TE: Additional Examples 1–5, pages 290–291	*Algebra 1 Review: Solving Inequalities* (p. 288)
Assignment Guide	▼ Informal Geometry Exercises: 1–9 ▼ Informal Geometry Exercises: 10–27, 32	▼ Exercises: 30, 33 ▼ Exercises: 28, 29, 31, 34–37 Extension: 38–41
Assessment Guide	Test Prep: Exercises 42– 49 Mixed Review: Exercises 50–61 TE: Lesson Quiz: 5-5	Ch. Review (pp. 297–299) Chapter Test (p. 300) Standardized Test Prep (p. 301)

RESOURCE OPTIONS

Teaching Resources	Chapter 5 Grab & Go File:
	    Practice 5-5, Reteaching 5-5
	    Enrichment 5-5
	Alternative Assessment, Form C
	Geometry Test Preparation
	Spanish Vocabulary Workbook and Study Skills
		All-in-One Student Workbook 5-5
		Spanish Practice Workbook 5-5
		Hands-On Activities 15
		Chapter 5 Test, Form F and G

Transparencies	Check Skills You'll Need 5-5 Additional Examples 5-5 Test-Taking Strategies 5, with practice sheet	Lesson Quiz 5-5 Student Edition Answers 5-5
Technology	Interactive Textbook Online ExamView Assessment Suite Teacher Express Presentation Express with QuickTake	Worksheets Online Success Tracker Online Intervention Mindpoint Quiz Show

Lesson 6-1

Classifying Quadrilaterals

INTRODUCE

Check Skills You'll Need (p. 306)
Students practice finding distance and slope, given the coordinates of two points.

FACILITATE

Math Background (p. 306)
Discuss with students the hierarchy of how quadrilaterals are classified in this lesson. Encourage students to think of other possible hierarchies.

Quick Check questions (pp. 307–308)
Assign these questions after each Example to see whether students understand the concepts presented.

Objectives
▼ Define and classify special types of quadrilaterals

New Vocabulary
parallelogram, rhombus, rectangle, square, kite, trapezoid, isosceles trapezoid

Standards
- NCTM Standards: Number and Operations, Algebra, Geometry, Measurement, Reasoning and Proof, Communication, Connections, Representation

	Informal Geometry Course	Optional Material
Teaching Guide	▼ *Classifying Special Quadrilaterals* (pp. 306–308) **Example 1:** Classifying a Quadrilateral **Example 2:** Classifying by Coordinate Methods **Example 3:** Using the Properties of Special Quadrilaterals TE: Additional Examples 1–3, page 307	
Assignment Guide	▼Informal Geometry Exercises: 1–26, 35, 36–41	▼Exercises: 27–34, 42–55 Extension: 56–59
Assessment Guide	Test Prep: Exercises 60–64 Mixed Review: Exercises 65–74 TE: Lesson Quiz: 6-1	

RESOURCE OPTIONS

Teaching Resources	Chapter 6 Grab & Go File: 　Practice 6-1, Reteaching 6-1 　Enrichment 6-1 Technology Activities 44 and 45 Spanish Vocabulary Workbook and Study Skills	All-in-One Student Workbook 6-1 Spanish Practice Workbook 6-1 Hands-On Activities 16
Transparencies	Check Skills You'll Need 6-1 Additional Examples 6-1 Classroom Aid, *Venn Diagrams and Graphic Organizer* Test-Taking Strategies 6, with practice sheet	Lesson Quiz 6-1 Student Edition Answers 6-1
Technology	Interactive Textbook Online ExamView Assessment Suite Teacher Express Presentation Express with QuickTake	Worksheets Online Success Tracker Online Intervention

Lesson 6-2

Properties of Parallelograms

INTRODUCE

Check Skills You'll Need (p. 312)
Students review naming congruent parts among two given triangles.

FACILITATE

Math Background (p. 312)
Remind students that because rectangles, rhombuses, and squares are all parallelograms, any property of a parallelogram can be applied to them.

Quick Check questions (pp. 313–315)
Assign these questions after each Example to see whether students understand the concepts presented.

Objectives
▼ Use relationships among sides and among angles of parallelograms
▼ Use relationships involving diagonals of parallelograms or transversals

New Vocabulary
consecutive angles

Standards
* NCTM Standards: Algebra, Geometry, Problem Solving, Reasoning and Proof, Communication, Connections, Representation

	Informal Geometry Course	Optional Material
Teaching Guide	▼ *Properties: Sides and Angles* (pp. 312–313) **Example 1:** Using Consecutive Angles **Example 2:** Using Algebra ▼ *Properties: Diagonals and Transversals* (pp. 314–315) **Example 3:** Using Algebra **Example 4:** Real-World Connection TE: Additional Examples 1–4, pages 313–314	*Guided Problem Solving* (p. 319)
Assignment Guide	▼ Informal Geometry Exercises: 1–13, 31–32 ▼ Informal Geometry Exercises: 14–30, 45–47	▼ Exercises: 33–39, 41–44, 48–50 Extension: 59, 60 ▼ Exercises: 40 Extension: 51–53
Assessment Guide	Test Prep: Exercises 54–60 Mixed Review: Exercises 61–67 TE: Lesson Quiz: 6-1	

RESOURCE OPTIONS

Teaching Resources	Chapter 6 Grab & Go File:
	    Practice 6-2, Reteaching 6-2
	    Enrichment 6-2
	Technology Activities 46
	Spanish Vocabulary Workbook and Study Skills
		All-in-One Student Workbook 6-2
		Spanish Practice Workbook 6-2
		Hands-On Activities 17

Transparencies	Check Skills You'll Need 6-2 Additional Examples 6-2 Test-Taking Strategies 6, with practice sheet	Lesson Quiz 6-2 Student Edition Answers 6-2
Technology	Interactive Textbook Online ExamView Assessment Suite Teacher Express Presentation Express with QuickTake	Worksheets Online Success Tracker Online Intervention

Lesson 6-3

Proving That a Quadrilateral Is a Parallelogram

NTRODUCE

Check Skills You'll Need (p. 321)
Students review finding the midpoint and slope of a segment on the coordinate plane.

Activity Lab (p. 320)
Students use geoboards to begin to discover Theorem 6-5 and Theorem 6-6.

FACILITATE

Math Background (p. 321)
Discuss with students how combining a theorem with its converse allows you to write the theorem as a biconditional using *if and only if.*

Quick Check questions (pp. 323–324)
Assign these questions after each Example to see whether students understand the concepts presented.

Objectives
▼ Determine whether a quadrilateral is a parallelogram

New Vocabulary
none

Standards
• NCTM Standards: Algebra, Geometry, Problem Solving, Reasoning and Proof, Communication, Connections, Representation

	Informal Geometry Course	**Optional Material**
Teaching Guide	▼ *Is the Quadrilateral a Parallelogram?* (pp. 321–324) **Example 1:** Finding Values for Parallelograms **Example 2:** Is the Quadrilateral a Parallelogram? **Example 3:** Real-World Connection TE: Additional Examples 1–3, pages 323–324	Activity Lab: *Hands-On: Geometry Models* (p. 320)
Assignment Guide	▼ Informal Geometry Exercises: 1–18	▼ Exercises: 19–25 Extension: 26–28
Assessment Guide	Test Prep: Exercises 29–32 Mixed Review: Exercises 33–39 Checkpoint Quiz 1 TE: Lesson Quiz: 6-3	

RESOURCE OPTIONS

Teaching Resources	Chapter 8 Grab & Go File:
	   Practice 6-3, Reteaching 6-3
	   Enrichment 6-3
	 Spanish Vocabulary Workbook and Study Skills
		All-in-One Student Workbook 6-3
		 Spanish Practice Workbook 6-3

Transparencies	Check Skills You'll Need 6-3 Additional Examples 6-3 Test-Taking Strategies 8, with practice sheet	Lesson Quiz 6-3 Student Edition Answers 6-3
Technology	Interactive Textbook Online ExamView Assessment Suite Teacher Express Presentation Express with QuickTake	Worksheets Online Success Tracker Online Intervention

Lesson 6-4

Special Parallelograms

INTRODUCE

Check Skills You'll Need (p. 329)
Students review finding angle measures and segment lengths in a parallelogram.

FACILITATE

Math Background (p. 329)
Discuss with students how using a less restrictive definition helps with establishing sufficient conditions.

Quick Check questions (pp. 330–332)
Assign these questions after each Example to see whether students understand the concepts presented.

Objectives
▼ Use properties of diagonals of rhombuses and rectangles
▼ Determine whether a parallelogram is a rhombus or a rectangle

New Vocabulary
none

Standards
• NCTM Standards: Geometry, Measurement, Data Analysis and Probability, Problem Solving, Reasoning and Proof, Communication, Connections, Representation

---

	Informal Geometry Course	Optional Material
Teaching Guide	▼ *Diagonals of Rhombuses and Rectangles* (pp. 329–331) **Example 1:** Finding Angle Measures **Example 2:** Finding Diagonal Length ▼ *Is the Parallelogram a Rhombus or a Rectangle?* (pp. 331–332) **Example 3:** Identifying Special Parallelograms **Example 4:** Real-World Connection TE: Additional Examples 1–4, pages 330–331	Activity Lab: *Technology: Diagonals of Parallelograms* (p. 328)
Assignment Guide	▼Informal Geometry Exercises: 1–15, 44–46 ▼Informal Geometry Exercises: 16–21	▼Exercises: 22, 50–59, ▼Exercises: 23–43, 47–49 Extension: 60–63
Assessment Guide	Test Prep: Exercises 64–66 Mixed Review: Exercises 67–76 TE: Lesson Quiz: 6-4	

RESOURCE OPTIONS

Teaching Resources	Chapter 6 Grab & Go File:
	    Practice 6-4, Reteaching 6-4
	    Enrichment 6-4
	 Spanish Vocabulary Workbook and Study Skills
		All-in-One Student Workbook 6-4
		 Spanish Practice Workbook 6-4
		 Technology Activities 47

Transparencies	Check Skills You'll Need 6-4 Additional Examples 6-4 Test-Taking Strategies 6, with practice sheet	Lesson Quiz 6-4 Student Edition Answers 6-4
Technology	Interactive Textbook Online ExamView Assessment Suite Teacher Express Presentation Express with QuickTake	Worksheets Online Success Tracker Online Intervention

Lesson 6-5

Trapezoids and Kites

INTRODUCE

Check Skills You'll Need (p. 336)
Students review using algebra to find the lengths of sides of trapezoids and kites.

FACILITATE

Math Background (p. 336)
Discuss with students how a kite can be described using two isosceles triangles or two intersecting circles.

Quick Check questions (pp. 337–338)
Assign these questions after each Example to see whether students understand the concepts presented.

Objectives
▼ Verify and use properties of trapezoids and kites

New Vocabulary
base angles of a trapezoid

Standards
• NCTM Standards: Geometry, Measurement, Problem Solving, Reasoning and Proof, Communication, Connections, Representation

	Informal Geometry Course	**Optional Material**
Teaching Guide	▼ *Properties of Trapezoids and Kites* (pp. 336–338) **Example 1:** Finding Angle Measures in Trapezoids **Example 2:** Real-World Connection **Example 3:** Finding Angle Measures in Kites TE: Additional Examples 1–3, pages 337–338	Activity Lab: *Technology: Quadrilaterals in Quadrilaterals* (p. 342)
Assignment Guide	▼ Informal Geometry Exercises: 1–16, 20–25	▼ Exercises: 17–19, 26–28, 29–38 Extension: 40–44
Assessment Guide	Test Prep: Exercises 45–50 Mixed Review: Exercises 51–56 TE: Lesson Quiz: 6-5	

RESOURCE OPTIONS

Teaching Resources	Chapter 6 Grab & Go File:
	  Practice 6-5, Reteaching 6-5
	  Enrichment 6-5
	  Spanish Vocabulary Workbook and Study Skills
		All-in-One Student Workbook 6-5
		Spanish Practice Workbook 6-5
		Hands-On Activities 18

Transparencies	Check Skills You'll Need 6-5 Additional Examples 6-5 Test-Taking Strategies 6, with practice sheet	Lesson Quiz 6-5 Student Edition Answers 6-5
Technology	Interactive Textbook Online ExamView Assessment Suite Teacher Express Presentation Express with QuickTake	Worksheets Online Success Tracker Online Intervention

Lesson 6-6

Placing Figures in the Coordinate Plane

ABOUT THIS LESSON

This lesson is not typically needed in an Informal Geometry Course. Check your state guidelines to see whether you should cover any of the Optional Material listed below.

Objectives
▼ Name coordinates of special figures by using their properties

New Vocabulary
none

Standards
• NCTM Standards: Algebra, Geometry, Reasoning and Proof, Communication, Connections, Representation

	Informal Geometry Course	**Optional Material**
Teaching Guide		▼*Naming Coordinates* (pp. 343–344) **Example 1:** Real-World Connection **Example 2:** Naming Coordinates TE: Additional Examples 1 and 2, page 344
Assignment Guide		▼Exercises: 1–27 Extension: 28–29
Assessment Guide	Mixed Review: Exercises 34–37	Test Prep: Exercises 30–33 Checkpoint Quiz 2 TE: Lesson Quiz: 6-6

RESOURCE OPTIONS

Teaching Resources	Chapter 6 Grab & Go File:
	  Practice 6-6, Reteaching 6-6
	  Enrichment 6-6
	Spanish Vocabulary Workbook and Study Skills
		All-in-One Student Workbook 6-6
		Spanish Practice Workbook 6-6

Transparencies	Check Skills You'll Need 6-6 Additional Examples 6-6 Classroom Aid, *Coordinate Plane* Test-Taking Strategies 6, with practice sheet	Lesson Quiz 6-6 Student Edition Answers 6-6
Technology	Interactive Textbook Online ExamView Assessment Suite Teacher Express Presentation Express with QuickTake	Worksheets Online Success Tracker Online Intervention

Lesson 6-7

Proofs Using Coordinate Geometry

ABOUT THIS LESSON

This lesson is not typically needed in an Informal Geometry Course. Check your state guidelines to see whether you should cover any of the Optional Material listed below.

Objectives
▼ Prove theorems using figures in the coordinate plane

New Vocabulary
midsegment of a trapezoid

Standards
• NCTM Standards: Algebra, Geometry, Measurement, Problem Solving, Reasoning and Proof, Communication, Connections, Representation

	Informal Geometry Course	Optional Material
Teaching Guide		▼*Building Proofs in the Coordinate Plane* (pp. 348–349) **Example 1:** Planning a Coordinate Geometry Proof **Example 2:** Real-World Connection TE: Additional Examples 1 and 2, page 349 Algebra 1 Review: Quadratics (pp. 354–355)
Assignment Guide		▼Exercises: 1–36 Extension: 37–41
Assessment Guide	Mixed Review: Exercises 46–53	Test Prep: Exercises 42–45 TE: Lesson Quiz: 6-7 Chapter Review (pp. 357–359) Chapter Test (p. 360) Standardized Test Prep (p. 361)

RESOURCE OPTIONS

Teaching Resources	Chapter 6 Grab & Go File: 　Practice 6-7, Reteaching 6-7 　Enrichment 6-7 Chapter 6 Test, Forms F and G Mid-Course Test, Forms D and E Spanish Vocabulary Workbook and Study Skills	All-in-One Student Workbook 6-7 Spanish Practice Workbook 6-7 Alternative Assessment, Form C Quarter 2 Test, Forms D and E Geometry Test Preparation
Transparencies	Check Skills You'll Need 6-7 Additional Examples 6-7 Classroom Aid, *Coordinate Plane* Test-Taking Strategies 6, with practice sheet	Lesson Quiz 6-7 Student Edition Answers 6-7
Technology	Interactive Textbook Online ExamView Assessment Suite Teacher Express Presentation Express with QuickTake	Worksheets Online Success Tracker Online Intervention Mindpoint Quiz Show

Lesson 7-1

Ratios and Proportions

INTRODUCE

Check Skills You'll Need (p. 366)
Students review simplifying ratios and drawing the midsegments of a triangle.

FACILITATE

Math Background (p. 366)
Remind students that in a proportion, the same units must be within each ratio or in comparable positions.

Quick Check questions (pp. 366-368)
Assign these questions after each Example to see whether students understand the concepts presented.

Objectives
▼ Write ratios and solve proportions

New Vocabulary
ratio, proportion, extended proportion, Cross-Product Property, scale drawing, scale

Standards
• NCTM Standards: Number and Operations, Algebra, Problem Solving, Communication, Connections, Representation

	Informal Geometry Course	Optional Material
Teaching Guide	▼ *Using Ratios and Proportions* (pp. 366–368) **Example 1:** Real-World Connection **Example 2:** Properties of Proportions **Example 3:** Solving for a Variable **Example 4:** Real-World Connection TE: Additional Examples 1–4, page 367	
Assignment Guide	▼ Informal Geometry Exercises: 1–29, 35–38	▼ Exercises: 30–34, 39–55 Extension: 56–61
Assessment Guide	Test Prep: Exercises 62–66 Mixed Review: Exercises 67–77 TE: Lesson Quiz: 7-1	

RESOURCE OPTIONS

Teaching Resources	Chapter 7 Grab & Go File: 　Practice 7-1, Reteaching 7-1 　Enrichment 7-1 Spanish Vocabulary Workbook and Study Skills	All-in-One Student Workbook 7-1 Spanish Practice Workbook 7-1
Transparencies	Check Skills You'll Need 7-1 Additional Examples 7-1 Test-Taking Strategies 7, with practice sheet	Lesson Quiz 7-1 Student Edition Answers 7-1
Technology	Interactive Textbook Online ExamView Assessment Suite Teacher Express Presentation Express with QuickTake	Worksheets Online Success Tracker Online Intervention

Lesson 7-2

Similar Polygons

INTRODUCE

Check Skills You'll Need (p. 373)
Students review naming congruent sides of triangles and solving proportions.

FACILITATE

Math Background (p. 373)
Discuss with students how ancient Greeks used the proportionality of sides to make indirect measurements.

Quick Check questions (pp. 373–375)
Assign these questions after each Example to see whether students understand the concepts presented.

Objectives
▽ Identify similar polygons
▽ Apply similar polygons

New Vocabulary
similar, similarity ratio, golden rectangle, golden ratio

Standards
• NCTM Standards: Algebra, Geometry, Problem Solving, Communication, Connections, Representation

	Informal Geometry Course	**Optional Material**
Teaching Guide	▽ *Similar Polygons* (pp. 373–374) **Example 1:** Understanding Similarity **Example 2:** Determining Similarity **Example 3:** Using Similar Figures ▽ *Applying Similar Polygons* (pp. 374–375) **Example 4:** Real-World Connection **Example 5:** Real-World Connection TE: Additional Examples 1–5, pages 374–375	*Algebra 1 Review: Solving Quadratic Equations* (p. 372) *Extension: Fractals* (pp. 380–381)
Assignment Guide	▽ Informal Geometry Exercises: 1–16, 21–26, 29, 30 ▽ Informal Geometry Exercises: 17–20	▽ Exercises: 27, 28, 32–39 Extension: 51 ▽ Exercises: 31, 40–50 Extension: 52
Assessment Guide	Test Prep: Exercises 53–56 Mixed Review: Exercises 57–66 Checkpoint Quiz 1 TE: Lesson Quiz: 7-2	

RESOURCE OPTIONS

Teaching Resources	Chapter 7 Grab & Go File:
	  Practice 7-2, Reteaching 7-2
	  Enrichment 7-2
	Spanish Vocabulary Workbook and Study Skills
		All-in-One Student Workbook 7-2
		Spanish Practice Workbook 7-2
		Hands-On Activities 22

Transparencies	Check Skills You'll Need 7-2 Additional Examples 7-2 Test-Taking Strategies 7, with practice sheet	Lesson Quiz 7-2 Student Edition Answers 7-2
Technology	Interactive Textbook Online ExamView Assessment Suite Teacher Express Presentation Express with QuickTake	Worksheets Online Success Tracker Online Intervention

Lesson 7-3

Proving Triangles Similar

INTRODUCE

Check Skills You'll Need (p. 382)
Students review triangle congruence theorems and postulates.

Activity (p. 382)
Students draw two triangles of different sizes, each with a 50° angle and a 60° angle, and measure the lengths of the sides to discover the Angle-Angle Similarity Postulate.

FACILITATE

Math Background (p. 382)
Discuss with students that after proving the Side-Splitter Theorem in Lesson 7-5, they can prove Angle-Angle Similarity as a theorem instead of a postulate.

Quick Check questions (pp. 383–385)
Assign these after each Example to see whether students understand the concepts presented.

Objectives
▼ Use AA, SAS, and SSS similarity statements
▼ Apply AA, SAS, and SSS similarity statements

New Vocabulary
indirect measurement

Standards
• NCTM Standards: Algebra, Geometry, Measurement, Problem Solving, Reasoning and Proof, Communication, Connections, Representation

	Informal Geometry Course	Optional Material
Teaching Guide	▼ *The AA Postulate and the SAS and SSS Similarity Theorems* (pp. 382–384) **Example 1:** Using the AA ~ Postulate **Example 2:** Using Similarity Theorems ▼ *Applying AA, SAS, and SSS Similarity* (pp. 382–385) **Example 3:** Finding Lengths in Similar Triangles **Example 4:** Real-World Connection TE: Additional Examples 1–4, pages 383–384	
Assignment Guide	▼ Informal Geometry Exercises: 1–9, 22, 23, 25–27 ▼ Informal Geometry Exercises: 10–19, 28	▼ Exercises: 24, 40 Extension: 42, 43 ▼ Exercises: 20, 21, 29–39, 41; Extension: 44
Assessment Guide	Test Prep: Exercises 45–48 Mixed Review: Exercises 49–57 TE: Lesson Quiz: 7-3	

RESOURCE OPTIONS

Teaching Resources	Chapter 7 Grab & Go File:
	  Practice 7-3, Reteaching 7-3
	  Enrichment 7-3
	Spanish Vocabulary Workbook and Study Skills
		All-in-One Student Workbook 7-3
		Spanish Practice Workbook 7-3

Transparencies	Check Skills You'll Need 7-3 Additional Examples 7-3 Test-Taking Strategies 7, with practice sheet	Lesson Quiz 7-3 Student Edition Answers 7-3
Technology	Interactive Textbook Online ExamView Assessment Suite Teacher Express Presentation Express with QuickTake	Worksheets Online Success Tracker Online Intervention

Lesson 7-4

Similarity in Right Triangles

INTRODUCE

Check Skills You'll Need (p. 391)
Students review solving proportions and drawing a right triangle and its altitude.

Hands-On Activity (p. 391)
Students use a rectangular sheet of paper to fold and cut out three right triangles. By measuring angles they begin to discover Theorem 7-3.

FACILITATE

Math Background (p. 391)
Discuss with students the algebraic formula for the geometric mean of two positive numbers.

Quick Check questions (pp. 392–393)
Assign these questions after each Example to see whether students understand the concepts presented.

Objectives
▼ Find and use relationships in similar right triangles

New Vocabulary
geometric mean

Standards
• NCTM Standards: Algebra, Geometry, Problem Solving, Reasoning and Proof, Communication, Connections, Representation

	Informal Geometry Course	Optional Material
Teaching Guide	▼ *Using Similarity in Right Triangles* (pp. 391–393) **Example 1:** Finding the Geometric Mean **Example 2:** Applying Corollaries 1 and 2 **Example 3:** Real-World Connection TE: Additional Examples 1–3, page 393	*Algebra 1 Review:* *Simplifying Radicals* *(p. 390)*
Assignment Guide	▼ Informal Geometry Exercises: 1–22, 26–29, 34–36	▼ Exercises: 23–25, 30–33, 37–51 Extension: 52–54
Assessment Guide	Test Prep: Exercises 55–59 Mixed Review: Exercises 60–67 TE: Lesson Quiz: 7-4	

RESOURCE OPTIONS

Teaching Resources	Chapter 7 Grab & Go File:
	    Practice 7-4, Reteaching 7-4
	    Enrichment 7-4
	Spanish Vocabulary Workbook and Study Skills
		All-in-One Student Workbook 7-4
		Spanish Practice Workbook 7-4
		Hands-On Activities 23

Transparencies	Check Skills You'll Need 7-4 Test-Taking Strategies 7, with practice sheet	Lesson Quiz 7-4
Technology	Interactive Textbook Online ExamView Assessment Suite Teacher Express Presentation Express with QuickTake	Worksheets Online Success Tracker Online Intervention

Lesson 7-5

Proportions in Triangles

INTRODUCE

Check Skills You'll Need (p. 398)
Students review finding missing values in similar triangles.

FACILITATE

Math Background (p. 398)
Discuss with students the relationships of the Side-Splitter Theorem with the Triangle Midsegment Theorem and the Triangle-Angle-Bisector Theorem.

Quick Check questions (pp. 399–400)
Assign these questions after each Example to see whether students understand the concepts presented.

Objectives
▼ Use the Side-Splitter Theorem
▼ Use the Triangle-Angle-Bisector Theorem

New Vocabulary
none

Standards
• NCTM Standards: Algebra, Geometry, Measurement, Problem Solving, Reasoning and Proof, Communication, Connections, Representation

---

	Informal Geometry Course	Optional Material
Teaching Guide	▼ *Using the Side-Splitter Theorem* (pp. 398–399) **Example 1:** Using the Side-Splitter Theorem **Example 2:** Real-World Connection ▼ *Using the Triangle-Angle-Bisector Theorem* (p. 400) **Example 3:** Using the Triangle-Angle-Bisector Theorem TE: Additional Examples 1–3, pages 399–400	*Technology: Exploring Proportions in Triangles* (p. 397) *Guided Problem Solving* (p. 405)
Assignment Guide	▼ Informal Geometry Exercises: 1–10, 25, 26 ▼ Informal Geometry Exercises: 11–24, 30, 32	▼ Exercises: 27, 28, 31, 33–39, 41–43 Extension: 45 ▼ Exercises: 29, 40, 44 Extension: 46, 47
Assessment Guide	Test Prep: Exercises 48–51 Mixed Review: Exercises 52–65 Checkpoint Quiz 2 TE: Lesson Quiz: 7-5	Chap. Rev. (pp. 407–409) Chap. Test (p. 410) Stand. Test Prep (p. 411)

RESOURCE OPTIONS

Teaching Resources	Chapter 7 Grab & Go File:
	     Practice 7-5, Reteaching 7-5
	     Enrichment 7-5
	 Alternative Assessment, Form C
	 Geometry Test Preparation
	 Spanish Vocabulary Workbook and Study Skills
		All-in-One Student Workbook 7-5
		 Spanish Practice Workbook 7-5
		 Hands-On Activities 24
		 Chapter 7 Test, Forms F and G

Transparencies	Check Skills You'll Need 7-5 Additional Examples 7-5 Test-Taking Strategies 7, with practice sheet	Lesson Quiz 7-5 Student Edition Answers 7-5
Technology	Interactive Textbook Online ExamView Assessment Suite Teacher Express Presentation Express with QuickTake	Worksheets Online Success Tracker Online Intervention Mindpoint Quiz Show

Lesson 8-1

The Pythagorean Theorem and Its Converse

INTRODUCE

Activity Lab (p. 416)
Students draw, cut out, and manipulate rectangles, right triangles, and squares to discover the Pythagorean Theorem.
Check Skills You'll Need (p. 417)
Students review squaring the lengths of the sides of triangles.

FACILITATE

Math Background (p. 417)
Discuss with students Goldbach's conjecture and the difficulty in proving it.
Quick Check questions (pp. 418–419)
Assign these after each Example to see whether students understand the concepts presented.

Objectives
▼ Use the Pythagorean Theorem
▼ Use the Converse of the Pythagorean Theorem

New Vocabulary
Pythagorean triple

Standards
• NCTM Standards: Algebra, Geometry, Measurement, Problem Solving, Reasoning and Proof, Communication, Connections, Representation

	Informal Geometry Course	Optional Material
Teaching Guide	▼ *The Pythagorean Theorem* (pp. 417–419) **Example 1:** Pythagorean Triples **Example 2:** Using Simplest Radical Form **Example 3:** Real-World Connection ▼ *The Converse of the Pythagorean Theorem* (p. 419) **Example 4:** Is It a Right Triangle? **Example 5:** Classifying Triangles as Acute, Obtuse, or Right TE: Additional Examples 1–5, pages 418–419	Activity Lab: *Hands-On: The Pythagorean Theorem* (p. 416) *Guided Problem Solving* (p. 424)
Assignment Guide	▼Informal Geometry Exercises: 1–17, 34–39 ▼Informal Geometry Exercises: 18–26, 30, 31	▼Exercises: 27–29, 32, 48–53, Extension: 54, 55–57 ▼Exercises: 33, 40–47 Extension: 58
Assessment Guide	Test Prep: Exercises 59–64 Mixed Review: Exercises 65–73 TE: Lesson Quiz: 8-1	

RESOURCE OPTIONS

Teaching Resources	Chapter 8 Grab & Go File:
	   Practice 8-1, Reteaching 8-1
	   Enrichment 8-1
	Spanish Vocabulary Workbook and Study Skills
		All-in-One Student Workbook 8-1
		Spanish Practice Workbook 8-1

Transparencies	Check Skills You'll Need 8-1 Additional Examples 8-1 Classroom Aid, *Table of Squares and Square Roots* Test-Taking Strategies 8, with practice sheet	Lesson Quiz 8-1 Student Edition Answers 8-1
Technology	Interactive Textbook Online ExamView Assessment Suite Teacher Express Presentation Express with QuickTake	Worksheets Online Success Tracker Online Intervention

Lesson 8-2

Special Right Triangles

INTRODUCE

Check Skills You'll Need (p. 425)
Students review using a protractor to find the measures of angles of a triangle.

FACILITATE

Math Background (p. 425)
Discuss with students that the ratios of 45°-45°-90° and 30°-60°-90° triangles will be a basis for the trigonometric functions of 30°, 45°, and 60° angles.

Quick Check questions (pp. 425–427)
Assign these questions after each Example to see whether students understand the concepts presented.

Objectives
▼ Use the properties of 45°-45°-90° triangles
▼ Use the properties of 30°-60°-90° triangles

New Vocabulary
none

Standards
• NCTM Standards: Algebra, Geometry, Measurement, Problem Solving, Communication, Connections, Representation

	Informal Geometry Course	Optional Material
Teaching Guide	▼ *Using 45°-45°-90° Triangles* (pp. 425–426) **Example 1:** Finding the Length of the Hypotenuse **Example 2:** Finding the Length of a Leg **Example 3:** Real-World Connection ▼ *Using 30°-60°-90° Triangles* (pp. 426–427) **Example 4:** Using the Length of One Side **Example 5:** Real-World Connection TE: Additional Examples 1–5, pages 426–427	
Assignment Guide	▼ Informal Geometry Exercises: 1–8, 21, 22 ▼ Informal Geometry Exercises: 9–20	▼ Exercises: 26 Extension: 27 ▼ Exercises: 23–25 Extension: 28
Assessment Guide	Test Prep: Exercises 29–32 Mixed Review: Exercises 33-–41 Checkpoint Quiz 1 TE: Lesson Quiz: 8-2	

RESOURCE OPTIONS

Teaching Resources	Chapter 8 Grab & Go File:
	  Practice 8-2, Reteaching 8-2
	  Enrichment 8-2
	Spanish Vocabulary Workbook and Study Skills
		All-in-One Student Workbook 8-2
		Spanish Practice Workbook 8-2

Transparencies	Check Skills You'll Need 8-2 Additional Examples 8-2 Test-Taking Strategies 8, with practice sheet	Lesson Quiz 8-2 Student Edition Answers 8-2
Technology	Interactive Textbook Online ExamView Assessment Suite Teacher Express Presentation Express with QuickTake	Worksheets Online Success Tracker Online Intervention

Lesson 8-3

The Tangent Ratio

INTRODUCE

Check Skills You'll Need (p. 432)
Students review finding ratios in triangles and solving proportions.

Activity (p. 432)
Students form groups and draw different-sized right triangles that have the same angle measures. By finding the ratio $\frac{\text{leg opposite } \angle A}{\text{leg adjacent } \angle A}$, they begin to discover the tangent ratio.

FACILITATE

Math Background (p. 432)
Explain to students that trigonometry dates back more than 2000 years to two Greek mathematicians.

Quick Check questions (pp. 433–434)
Assign these questions after each Example to see whether students understand the concepts presented.

Objectives
▼ Use tangent ratios to determine side lengths in triangles

New Vocabulary
tangent

Standards
• NCTM Standards: Geometry, Problem Solving, Reasoning and Proof, Communication, Connections, Representation

	Informal Geometry Course	**Optional Material**
Teaching Guide	▼*Using Tangent in Triangles* (pp. 432–434) **Example 1:** Writing Tangent Ratios **Example 2:** Real-World Connection **Example 3:** Using the Inverse of Tangent TE: Additional Examples 1–3, pages 433–434	Activity Lab: *Hands-On The Staff and Stadiascope* (p. 431)
Assignment Guide	▼Informal Geometry Exercises: 1–20, 23, 24	▼Exercises: 21–22, 25–45 Extension: 46–58
Assessment Guide	Test Prep: Exercises 59–65 Mixed Review: Exercises 66–70 TE: Lesson Quiz: 8-3	

RESOURCE OPTIONS

Teaching Resources	Chapter 8 Grab & Go File:
	    Practice 8-3, Reteaching 8-3
	    Enrichment 8-3
	Spanish Vocabulary Workbook and Study Skills
		All-in-One Student Workbook 8-3
		Spanish Practice Workbook 8-3
		Hands-On Activities 25

Transparencies	Check Skills You'll Need 8-3 Additional Examples 8-3 Classroom Aid, *The Tangent Ratio* Test-Taking Strategies 8, with practice sheet	Lesson Quiz 8-3 Student Edition Answers 8-3
Technology	Interactive Textbook Online ExamView Assessment Suite Teacher Express Presentation Express with QuickTake	Worksheets Online Success Tracker Online Intervention

Lesson 8-4

Sine and Cosine Ratios

INTRODUCE

Check Skills You'll Need (p. 439)
Students review using the tangent ratio to find
lengths in a right triangle.

FACILITATE

Math Background (p. 439)
Discuss with students the use of sine and cosine in
a unit circle.

Quick Check questions (pp. 439–440)
Assign these questions after each Example to see
whether students understand the concepts
presented.

Objectives
▼ Use sine and cosine to determine side
lengths in triangles

New Vocabulary
sine, cosine, identity

Standards
• NCTM Standards: Geometry, Problem
Solving, Communication, Connections,
Representation

	Informal Geometry Course	Optional Material
Teaching Guide	▼ *Using Sine and Cosine in Triangles* (pp. 439–440) **Example 1:** Writing Sine and Cosine Ratios **Example 2:** Real-World Connection **Example 3:** Using the Inverse of Cosine and Sine TE: Additional Examples 1–3, page 440	Activity Lab: *Technology Exploring Trigonometric Ratios* (p. 438)
Assignment Guide	▼ Informal Geometry Exercises: 1–16, 21, 26	▼ Exercises: 17–20, 22–25, 27–30 Extension: 31–36
Assessment Guide	Test Prep: Exercises 37–40 Mixed Review: Exercises 41–47 TE: Lesson Quiz: 8-4	

RESOURCE OPTIONS

Teaching Resources	Chapter 8 Grab & Go File:
	    Practice 8-4, Reteaching 8-4
	    Enrichment 8-4
	Spanish Vocabulary Workbook and Study Skills
		All-in-One Student Workbook 8-4
		Spanish Practice Workbook 8-4
		Hands-On Activities 26

Transparencies	Check Skills You'll Need 8-4 Additional Examples 8-4 Classroom Aid, *Sine and Cosine Ratios* Test-Taking Strategies 8, with practice sheet	Lesson Quiz 8-4 Student Edition Answers 8-4
Technology	Interactive Textbook Online ExamView Assessment Suite Teacher Express Presentation Express with QuickTake	Worksheets Online Success Tracker Online Intervention

Lesson 8-5

•••
Angles of Elevation and Depression

INTRODUCE

Check Skills You'll Need (p. 445)
Students review naming congruent angles, complementary angles, and supplementary angles using the properties of two parallel lines cut by a transversal.

FACILITATE

Math Background (p. 445)
Explain to students that indirect measurement has been used for more than 2000 years.

Quick Check questions (pp. 445-446)
Assign these questions after each Example to see whether students understand the concepts presented.

Objectives
▼ Use angles of elevation and depression to solve problems

New Vocabulary
angle of elevation, angle of depression

Standards
• NCTM Standards: Algebra, Geometry, Measurement, Problem Solving, Reasoning and Proof, Communication, Connections, Representation

	Informal Geometry Course	Optional Material
Teaching Guide	▼ *Using Angles of Elevation and Depression* (pp. 445–446) **Example 1:** Identifying Angles of Elevation and Depression **Example 2:** Real-World Connection **Example 3:** Real-World Connection TE: Additional Examples 1–3, page 446	Activity Lab: *Hands-On: Measuring from Afar* (p. 444) *Guided Problem Solving* (p. 451)
Assignment Guide	▼ Informal Geometry Exercises: 1–16	▼ Exercises: 17–28 Extension: 29–30
Assessment Guide	Test Prep: Exercises 31–34 Mixed Review: Exercises 35–40 Checkpoint Quiz 2 TE: Lesson Quiz: 8-5	

RESOURCE OPTIONS

Teaching Resources	Chapter 8 Grab & Go File:
	    Practice 8-5, Reteaching 8-5
	    Enrichment 8-5
	Spanish Vocabulary Workbook and Study Skills
		All-in-One Student Workbook 8-5
		Spanish Practice Workbook 8-5

Transparencies	Check Skills You'll Need 8-5 Additional Examples 8-5 Test-Taking Strategies 8, with practice sheet	Lesson Quiz 8-5 Student Edition Answers 8-5
Technology	Interactive Textbook Online ExamView Assessment Suite Teacher Express Presentation Express with QuickTake	Worksheets Online Success Tracker Online Intervention

Lesson 8-6

Vectors

ABOUT THIS LESSON

This lesson is not typically needed in an Informal Geometry Course. Check your state guidelines to see whether you should cover any of the Optional Material listed below.

Objectives
▼ Describe vectors
▼ Solve problems that involve vector addition

New Vocabulary
vector, magnitude, initial point, terminal point, resultant

Standards
• NCTM Standards: Number and Operations, Algebra, Geometry, Problem Solving, Communication, Connections, Representation

	Informal Geometry Course	Optional Material
Teaching Guide		▼*Describing Vectors* (pp. 452–453) **Example 1:** Describing a Vector **Example 2:** Describing a Vector Direction **Example 3:** Real-World Connection ▼*Adding Vectors* (pp. 454–455) **Example 4:** Adding Vectors **Example 5:** Real-World Connection TE: Additional Examples 1–5, pages 453–454
Assignment Guide		▼Exercises: 1–16, 29, 30, 32, 33, 40, 45, 46 Extension: 49 ▼Exercises: 17–28, 31, 34–39, 41–44, 47, 48 Extension: 50–52
Assessment Guide	Mixed Review: Exercises 56–60	Test Prep: Exercises 53–55 TE: Lesson Quiz: 8-6 Chapter Review: (pp. 461–463) Chapter Test, (p. 464) Standardized Test Prep (p. 465)

RESOURCE OPTIONS

Teaching Resources	Chapter 8 Grab & Go File:
	   Practice 8-6, Reteaching 8-6
	   Enrichment 8-6
	Alternative Assessment, Form C
	Geometry Test Preparation
	Spanish Vocabulary Workbook and Study Skills
		All-in-One Student Workbook 8-6
		Spanish Practice Workbook 8-6
		Hands-On Activities 27
		Chapter 8 Test, Forms F and G

Transparencies	Check Skills You'll Need 8-6 Additional Examples 8-6 Test-Taking Strategies 8, with practice sheet	Lesson Quiz 8-6 Student Edition Answers 8-6
Technology	Interactive Textbook Online ExamView Assessment Suite Teacher Express Presentation Express with QuickTake	Worksheets Online Success Tracker Online Intervention Mindpoint Quiz Show

Lesson 9-1

Translations

INTRODUCE

Check Skills You'll Need (p. 470)
Students review identifying congruent parts of congruent triangles..

FACILITATE

Math Background (p. 470)
Explain to students how transformations can be described as a one-to-one correspondence between two sets of points.

Quick Check questions (pp. 470–472)
Assign these questions after each Example to see whether students understand the concepts presented.

Objectives
▼ Identify isometries
▼ Find translation images of figures

New Vocabulary
transformation, preimage, image, isometry, translation, composition

Standards
- NCTM Standards: Geometry, Problem Solving, Communication, Connections, Representation

	Informal Geometry Course	Optional Material
Teaching Guide	▼*Identifying Isometries* (pp. 470–471) **Example 1:** Identifying Isometries **Example 2:** Naming Images and Corresponding Parts ▼*Translations* (pp. 471–472) **Example 3:** Finding a Translation Image **Example 4:** Writing a Rule to Describe a Translation **Example 5:** Real-World Connection TE: Additional Examples 1–5, pages 471–472	
Assignment Guide	▼Informal Geometry Exercises:s 1–6 ▼Informal Geometry Exercises: 7–19	▼Exercises: 20–34 Extension: 35–36
Assessment Guide	Test Prep: Exercises 37–41 Mixed Review: Exercises 42–46 TE: Lesson Quiz: 9-1	

RESOURCE OPTIONS

Teaching Resources	Chapter 9 Grab & Go File:
	    Practice 9-1, Reteaching 9-1
	    Enrichment 9-1
	Spanish Vocabulary Workbook and Study Skills
		All-in-One Student Workbook 9-1
		Spanish Practice Workbook 9-1

Transparencies	Check Skills You'll Need 9-1 Additional Examples 9-1 Test-Taking Strategies 9, with practice sheet	Lesson Quiz 9-1 Student Edition Answers 9-1
Technology	Interactive Textbook Online ExamView Assessment Suite Teacher Express Presentation Express with QuickTake	Worksheets Online Success Tracker Online Intervention

Lesson 9-2

Reflections

INTRODUCE

Check Skills You'll Need (p. 478)
Students review writing equations of lines perpendicular to a given line.

FACILITATE

Math Background (p. 478)
Explain to students how reflections can be demonstrated using mirrors.

Quick Check questions (p. 479)
Assign these questions after each Example to see whether students understand the concepts presented.

Objectives
▼ Find reflection images of figures

New Vocabulary
reflection

Standards
- NCTM Standards: Geometry, Problem Solving, Communication, Connections, Representation

	Informal Geometry Course	Optional Material
Teaching Guide	▼*Finding Reflection Images* (pp. 478–479) **Example 1:** Finding Reflection Images **Example 2:** Drawing Reflection Images **Example 3:** Real-World Connection TE: Additional Examples 1–3, page 479	Activity Lab: *Hands-On: Paper Folding and Reflections* (p. 477)
Assignment Guide	▼Informal Geometry Exercises: 1–21	▼Exercises: 22–37 Extension: 38–46
Assessment Guide	Test Prep: Exercises 47–52 Mixed Review: Exercises 53–58 TE: Lesson Quiz: 9-2	

RESOURCE OPTIONS

Teaching Resources	Chapter 9 Grab & Go File:
	   Practice 9-2, Reteaching 9-2
	   Enrichment 9-2
	Spanish Vocabulary Workbook and Study Skills
		All-in-One Student Workbook 9-2
		Spanish Practice Workbook 9-2
		Hands-On Activities 34

Transparencies	Check Skills You'll Need 9-2 Additional Examples 9-2 Test-Taking Strategies 9, with practice sheet	Lesson Quiz 9-2 Student Edition Answers 9-2
Technology	Interactive Textbook Online ExamView Assessment Suite Teacher Express Presentation Express with QuickTake	Worksheets Online Success Tracker Online Intervention

Lesson 9-3

Rotations

INTRODUCE

Check Skills You'll Need (p. 483)
Students review finding angle measures of regular polygons.

Hands-On Activity (p. 483)
Using tracing paper and the given image, students practice using rotations to create a design.

FACILITATE

Math Background (p. 483)
Remind students that a rotation function is uniquely determined by the center of rotation and angle of rotation.

Quick Check questions (pp. 484–485)
Assign these questions after each Example to see whether students understand the concepts presented.

Objectives
▼ Draw and identify rotation images of figures

New Vocabulary
rotation, center of a regular polygon

Standards
• NCTM Standards: Geometry, Problem Solving, Communication, Connections, Representation

	Informal Geometry Course	Optional Material
Teaching Guide	▼ *Drawing and Identifying Rotation Images* (pp. 483–485) **Example 1:** Drawing a Rotation Image **Example 2:** Identifying a Rotation Image **Example 3:** Real-World Connection **Example 4:** Compositions of Rotations TE: Additional Examples 1–4, pages 484–485	*Guided Problem Solving* (p. 489) Activity Lab: *Hands-On: Tracing Paper and Transformations* (p. 491)
Assignment Guide	▼Informal Geometry Exercises: 1–26	▼Exercises: 27–33 Extension: 34
Assessment Guide	Test Prep: Exercises 35–39 Mixed Review: Exercises 40–47 Checkpoint Quiz 1 TE: Lesson Quiz: 9-3	

RESOURCE OPTIONS

Teaching Resources	Chapter 9 Grab & Go File:
	    Practice 9-3, Reteaching 9-3
	    Enrichment 9-3
	Spanish Vocabulary Workbook and Study Skills
		All-in-One Student Workbook 9-3
		Spanish Practice Workbook 9-3

Transparencies	Check Skills You'll Need 9-3 Additional Examples 9-3 Test-Taking Strategies 9, with practice sheet	Lesson Quiz 9-3 Student Edition Answers 9-3
Technology	Interactive Textbook Online ExamView Assessment Suite Teacher Express Presentation Express with QuickTake	Worksheets Online Success Tracker Online Intervention

Lesson 9-4

Symmetry

INTRODUCE

Check Skills You'll Need (p. 492)
Students review using rotations and reflections to
identify images.

FACILITATE

Math Background (p. 492)
Discuss with students the symmetry group of a
figure.
Quick Check questions (pp. 492–493)
Assign these questions after each Example to see
whether students understand the concepts
presented.

Objectives
▼ Identify the type of symmetry in a figure

New Vocabulary
symmetry, reflectional symmetry, line
symmetry, rotational symmetry, point symmetry

Standards
• NCTM Standards: Geometry, Problem
Solving, Communication, Connections,
Representation

	Informal Geometry Course	**Optional Material**
Teaching Guide	▼*Identifying Types of Symmetry in Figures* (pp. 492–493) **Example 1:** Identifying Lines of Symmetry **Example 2:** Identifying Rotational Symmetry **Example 3:** Real-World Connection TE: Additional Examples 1–3, page 493	
Assignment Guide	▼Informal Geometry Exercises: 1–23, 25–32	▼Exercises: 24, 33–44 Extension: 45–50
Assessment Guide	Test Prep: Exercises 51–56 Mixed Review: Exercises 57–61 TE: Lesson Quiz: 9-4	

RESOURCE OPTIONS

Teaching Resources	Chapter 9 Grab & Go File:
	  Practice 9-4, Reteaching 9-4
	  Enrichment 9-4
	Spanish Vocabulary Workbook and Study Skills
		All-in-One Student Workbook 9-4
		Spanish Practice Workbook 9-4
		Hands-On Activities 35

Transparencies	Check Skills You'll Need 9-4 Additional Examples 9-4 Test-Taking Strategies 9, with practice sheet	Lesson Quiz 9-4 Student Edition Answers 9-4
Technology	Interactive Textbook Online ExamView Assessment Suite Teacher Express Presentation Express with QuickTake	Worksheets Online Success Tracker Online Intervention

Lesson 9-5

Dilations

ABOUT THIS LESSON

This lesson is not typically needed in an Informal Geometry Course. Check your state guidelines to see whether you should cover any of the Optional Material listed below.

Objectives
▼ Locate dilation images of figures

New Vocabulary
dilation, enlargement, reduction,

Standards
• NCTM Standards: Number and Operations, Geometry, Measurement, Problem Solving, Communication, Connections, Representation

	Informal Geometry Course	Optional Material
Teaching Guide		▼ *Locating Dilation Images* (pp. 498–499) **Example 1:** Finding a Scale Factor **Example 2:** Real-World Connection **Example 3:** Graphing Dilation Images TE: Additional Examples 1–3, page 499 Extension: Transformations Using Vectors and Matrices (pp. 504–505)
Assignment Guide		▼ Exercises: 1–61 Extension: 62–66
Assessment Guide	Mixed Review: Exercises 72–81	Test Prep: Exercises 67–71 TE: Lesson Quiz: 9-5

RESOURCE OPTIONS

Teaching Resources	Chapter 9 Grab & Go File: 　Practice 9-5, Reteaching 9-5 　Enrichment 9-5 Spanish Vocabulary Workbook and Study Skills	All-in-One Student Workbook 9-5 Spanish Practice Workbook 9-5
Transparencies	Check Skills You'll Need 9-5 Additional Examples 9-5 Test-Taking Strategies 9, with practice sheet	Lesson Quiz 9-5 Student Edition Answers 9-5
Technology	Interactive Textbook Online ExamView Assessment Suite Teacher Express Presentation Express with QuickTake	Worksheets Online Success Tracker Online Intervention

Lesson 9-6

Compositions of Reflections

ABOUT THIS LESSON

This lesson is not typically needed in an Informal Geometry Course. Check your state guidelines to see whether you should cover any of the Optional Material listed below.

Objectives
▼ Use a composition of reflections
▼ Identify glide reflections

New Vocabulary
glide reflection

Standards
• NCTM Standards: Geometry, Problem Solving, Communication, Connections, Representation

	Informal Geometry Course	Optional Material
Teaching Guide		▼ *Composition of Reflections* (pp. 506–507) **Example 1:** Recognizing the Transformation **Example 2:** Composition of Reflections Across Parallel Lines **Example 3:** Composition of Reflections in Intersecting Lines ▼ *Glide Reflections* (pp. 508–509) **Example 4:** Finding a Glide Reflection Image **Example 5:** Classifying Isometries TE: Additional Examples 1–5, pages 507–508 Activity Lab: *Technology: Kaleidoscopes* (p. 513)
Assignment Guide		▼ Exercises: 1–9, 25, 26, 31–34 Extension: 46–48, 50 ▼ Exercises: 10–24, 27–30, 35–44 Extension: 45, 49, 51–54
Assessment Guide	Mixed Review: Exercises 59–67	Test Prep: Exercises 55–58 TE: Lesson Quiz: 9-6

RESOURCE OPTIONS

Teaching Resources	Chapter 9 Grab & Go File:
	    Practice 9-6, Reteaching 9-6
	    Enrichment 9-6
	 Spanish Vocabulary Workbook and Study Skills
		All-in-One Student Workbook 9-6
		 Spanish Practice Workbook 9-6

Transparencies	Check Skills You'll Need 9-6 Additional Examples 9-6 Test-Taking Strategies 9, with practice sheet	Lesson Quiz 9-6 Student Edition Answers 9-6
Technology	Interactive Textbook Online ExamView Assessment Suite Teacher Express Presentation Express with QuickTake	Worksheets Online Success Tracker Online Intervention

Lesson 9-7

Tessellations

INTRODUCE

Check Skills You'll Need (p. 515)
Students review classifying and finding angle measures of regular polygons.

FACILITATE

Math Background (p. 515)
Discuss with students astronomer Johannes Kepler's contributions to the discovery of tessellations.

Quick Check questions (pp. 515–517)
Assign these after Examples 1 and 2 to see if students understand the concepts presented. Objective 2 is not typically needed in an Informal Geometry Course. Check your state guidelines to see if you should cover any of the Optional Material listed for Objective 2.

Objectives

▼ Identify transformations in tessellations, and figures that will tessellate
▼ Identify symmetries in tessellations

New Vocabulary

tessellation, tiling, translational symmetry, glide reflectional symmetry

Standards

- NCTM Standards: Algebra, Geometry, Problem Solving, Communication, Connections, Representation

	Informal Geometry Course	**Optional Material**
Teaching Guide	▼*Identifying Transformations in Tessellations* (pp. 515–516) **Example 1:** Identifying the Transformation in a Tessellation **Example 2:** Determining Figures That Will Tessellate TE: Additional Examples 1 and 2, pages 516–517	▼*Identifying Symmetries in Tessellations* (pp. 516–517) **Example 3:** Identifying Symmetries in Tessellations Activity Lab: *Hands-On: Frieze Patterns* (p. 514)
Assignment Guide	▼Informal Geometry Exercises: 1–10, 14–17	▼Exercises: 18–22 Extension: 27–39 ▼Exercises: 11–13, 23–26 Extension: 40, 41
Assessment Guide	Mixed Review: Exercises 47–56	Test Prep: Exercises 42–46 Checkpoint Quiz 2 TE: Lesson Quiz: 9-7 Chap. Rev. (pp. 523–525) Chapter Test, (p. 526) Stand. Test Prep (p. 527)

RESOURCE OPTIONS

Teaching Resources	Chapter 9 Grab & Go File: Practice 9-7, Reteaching 9-7 Enrichment 9-7 Alternative Assessment, Form C Quarter 3 Test, Forms D and E Spanish Vocabulary Workbook and Study Skills	All-in-One Student Workbook 9-7 Spanish Practice Workbook 9-7 Hands-On Activities 36 Chapter 9 Test, Forms F and G Geometry Test Preparation
Transparencies	Check Skills You'll Need 9-7 Additional Examples 9-7 Test-Taking Strategies 9, with practice sheet	Lesson Quiz 9-7 Student Edition Answers 9-7
Technology	Interactive Textbook Online ExamView Assessment Suite Teacher Express Presentation Express with QuickTake	Worksheets Online Success Tracker Online Intervention Mindpoint Quiz Show

Lesson 10-1

Areas of Parallelograms and Triangles

INTRODUCE

Check Skills You'll Need (p. 534)
Students review finding the area of squares and rectangles.

Activity Lab (pp. 532–533)
Students manipulate a rectangle to discover the relationship between the formulas for the area of a rectangle and for the area of a parallelogram.

FACILITATE

Math Background (p. 534)
Discuss with students why the area of a rectangle is often in terms of base and height, not length and width.

Quick Check questions (pp. 535–536)
Assign these questions after each Example to see whether students understand the concepts presented.

Objectives
▼ Find the area of a parallelogram
▼ Find the area of a triangle

New Vocabulary
base of a parallelogram, altitude of a parallelogram, height of a parallelogram, base of a triangle, height of a triangle

Standards
• NCTM Standards: Algebra, Geometry, Measurement, Problem Solving, Communication, Connections, Representation

	Informal Geometry Course	Optional Material
Teaching Guide	▼ *Area of a Parallelogram* (pp. 534–535) **Example 1:** Finding the Area of a Parallelogram **Example 2:** Finding a Missing Dimension ▼ *Area of a Triangle* (pp. 535–536) **Example 3:** Finding the Area of a Triangle **Example 4:** Real-World Connection TE: Additional Examples 1–4, pages 535–536	Activity Lab: *Hands-On: Transforming to Find Area* (pp. 532–533)
Assignment Guide	▼Informal Geometry Exercises: 1–6, 11–16 ▼Informal Geometry Exercises: 7–10, 17–23	▼Exercises: 24–28 ▼Exercises: 29–36 Extension: 37–39
Assessment Guide	Test Prep: Exercises 40–44 Mixed Review: Exercises 45–55 TE: Lesson Quiz: 10-1	

RESOURCE OPTIONS

Teaching Resources	Chapter 10 Grab & Go File:
	   Practice 10-1, Reteaching 10-1
	   Enrichment 10-1
	Technology Activities 48
	Spanish Vocabulary Workbook and Study Skills
		All-in-One Student Workbook 10-1
		Spanish Practice Workbook 10-1
		Hands-On Activities 19

Transparencies	Check Skills You'll Need 10-1 Additional Examples 10-1 Test-Taking Strategies 10, with practice sheet	Lesson Quiz 10-1 Student Edition Answers 10-1
Technology	Interactive Textbook Online ExamView Assessment Suite Teacher Express Presentation Express with QuickTake	Worksheets Online Success Tracker Online Intervention

Lesson 10-2

•••

Areas of Trapezoids, Rhombuses, and Kites

INTRODUCE

Check Skills You'll Need (p. 540)
Students review the area formulas for triangles
and rectangles.

Activity Lab (pp. 532–533)
Students draw, cut out, and manipulate two
congruent trapezoids, forming a parallelogram, to
discover the formula for the area of a trapezoid.

FACILITATE

Math Background (p. 540)
Remind students that the area formulas for
triangles and parallelograms can help them arrive
at the formulas for the areas of trapezoids,
rhombuses, and kites.

Quick Check questions (pp. 540–542)
Assign these questions after each Example to see
whether students understand the concepts
presented.

> **Objectives**
> ▼ Find the area of a trapezoid
> ▼ Find the area of a rhombus or a kite
>
> **New Vocabulary**
> height of a trapezoid
>
> **Standards**
> • NCTM Standards: Number and Operations,
>   Algebra, Geometry, Measurement, Problem
>   Solving, Communication, Connections,
>   Representation

	Informal Geometry Course	**Optional Material**
Teaching Guide	▼ *Area of a Trapezoid* (pp. 540–541) **Example 1:** Real-World Connection **Example 2:** Finding Area Using a Right Triangle ▼ *Finding Areas of Rhombuses and Kites* (pp. 541–542) **Example 3:** Finding the Area of a Kite **Example 4:** Finding the Area of a Rhombus TE: Additional Examples 1–4, pages 541–542	Activity Lab: *Hands-On: Transforming to Find Area* (pp. 532–533)
Assignment Guide	▼ Informal Geometry Exercises: 1–10, 17–18 ▼ Informal Geometry Exercises: 11–16, 25–28	▼ Exercises: 20–24, 33 Extension: 35, 36 ▼ Exercises: 19, 29–32, 34 Extension: 37
Assessment Guide	Test Prep: Exercises 38–42 Mixed Review: Exercises 43–48 TE: Lesson Quiz: 10-2	

RESOURCE OPTIONS

Teaching Resources	Chapter 10 Grab & Go File:
	    Practice 10-2, Reteaching 10-2
	    Enrichment 10-2
	 Spanish Vocabulary Workbook and Study Skills
		All-in-One Student Workbook 10-2
		 Spanish Practice Workbook 10-2
		 Hands-On Activities 20

Transparencies	Check Skills You'll Need 10-2 Additional Examples 10-2 Test-Taking Strategies 10, with practice sheet	Lesson Quiz 10-2 Student Edition Answers 10-2
Technology	Interactive Textbook Online ExamView Assessment Suite Teacher Express Presentation Express with QuickTake	Worksheets Online Success Tracker Online Intervention

Lesson 10-3

Areas of Regular Polygons

INTRODUCE

Check Skills You'll Need (p. 546)
Students review finding the areas of squares and equilateral triangles and the perimeter of regular polygons.

FACILITATE

Math Background (p. 546)
Show students how to create a regular n-gon inscribed in a circle by using $\frac{360°}{n}$ to find each angle measure.

Quick Check questions (pp. 546–547)
Assign these questions after each Example to see whether students understand the concepts presented.

Objectives
▼ Find the area of a regular polygon

New Vocabulary
radius of a regular polygon, apothem

Standards
• NCTM Standards: Algebra, Geometry, Measurement, Problem Solving, Reasoning and Proof, Communication, Connections, Representation

---

	Informal Geometry Course	Optional Material
Teaching Guide	▼ *Areas of Regular Polygons* (pp. 546–547) **Example 1:** Finding Angle Measures **Example 2:** Finding the Area of a Regular Polygon **Example 3:** Real-World Connection TE: Additional Examples 1–3, page 547	*Guided Problem Solving* (p. 552)
Assignment Guide	▼Informal Geometry Exercises: 1–24	▼Exercises 25–35 Extension: 36–38
Assessment Guide	Test Prep: Exercises 39–43 Mixed Review: Exercises 44–50 TE: Lesson Quiz: 10-3	

RESOURCE OPTIONS

Teaching Resources	Chapter 10 Grab & Go File:
	    Practice 10-3, Reteaching 10-3
	    Enrichment 10-3
	 Spanish Vocabulary Workbook and Study Skills
		All-in-One Student Workbook 10-3
		 Spanish Practice Workbook 10-3

Transparencies	Check Skills You'll Need 10-3 Additional Examples 10-3 Classroom Aid, *Geometric Shapes I* Test-Taking Strategies 10, with practice sheet	Lesson Quiz 10-3 Student Edition Answers 10-3
Technology	Interactive Textbook Online ExamView Assessment Suite Teacher Express Presentation Express with QuickTake	Worksheets Online Success Tracker Online Intervention

Lesson 10-4

Perimeters and Areas of Similar Figures

INTRODUCE

Check Skills You'll Need (p. 553)
Students review finding perimeter and area of figures.

Hands-On Activity (p. 553)
Students draw and calculate perimeter and area of four similar rectangles. They begin to discover Theorem 10-7 by finding the ratio of their perimeters and areas.

FACILITATE

Math Background (p. 553)
Show students how to prove the similarity ratio of the area of two similar triangles by drawing altitudes and using the Transitive Property.

Quick Check questions (pp. 554–555)
Assign these after each Example to see whether students understand the concepts presented.

Objectives
▼ Find the perimeters and areas of similar figures

New Vocabulary
none

Standards
• NCTM Standards: Number and Operations, Algebra, Geometry, Measurement, Problem Solving, Reasoning and Proof, Communication, Connections, Representation

	Informal Geometry Course	**Optional Material**
Teaching Guide	▼ *Finding Perimeters and Areas of Similar Figures* (pp. 553–555) **Example 1:** Finding Ratios in Similar Figures **Example 2:** Finding Areas Using Similar Figures **Example 3:** Real-World Connection **Example 4:** Finding Similarity and Perimeter Ratios TE: Additional Examples 1–4, page 555	
Assignment Guide	▼ Informal Geometry Exercises: 1–22, 35–37	▼ Exercises: 23–34, 38–40 Extension: 41–44
Assessment Guide	Test Prep: Exercises 45–49 Mixed Review: Exercises 50–61 TE: Lesson Quiz: 10-4	

RESOURCE OPTIONS

Teaching Resources	Chapter 10 Grab & Go File:
	   Practice 10-4, Reteaching 10-4
	   Enrichment 10-4
	Chapter 10 Test, Forms D and E
	Spanish Vocabulary Workbook and Study Skills
		All-in-One Student Workbook 10-4
		Spanish Practice Workbook 10-4
		Alternative Assessment, Form C
		Geometry Test Preparation

Transparencies	Check Skills You'll Need 10-4 Additional Examples 10-4 Test-Taking Strategies 10, with practice sheet	Lesson Quiz 10-4 Student Edition Answers 10-4
Technology	Interactive Textbook Online ExamView Assessment Suite Teacher Express Presentation Express with QuickTake	Worksheets Online Success Tracker Online Intervention

Lesson 10-5

Trigonometry and Area

ABOUT THIS LESSON

This lesson is not typically needed in an Informal Geometry Course. Check your state guidelines to see whether you should cover any of the Optional Material listed below.

Objectives

▼ Find areas of regular polygons using trigonometry
▼ Find areas of triangles using trigonometry

New Vocabulary

Standards

- NCTM Standards: Algebra, Geometry, Measurement, Problem Solving, Communication, Connections, Representation

	Informal Geometry Course	**Optional Material**
Teaching Guide		▼ *Finding Areas of a Regular Polygon* (pp. 559–560) **Example 1:** Finding Area **Example 2:** Real-World Connection ▼ *Finding the Area of a Triangle* (pp. 560–561) **Example 3:** Real-World Connection TE: Additional Examples 1–3, pages 560–561 Extension: *Law of Sines and Cosines* (p. 565)
Assignment Guide		▼Exercises: 1–10, 18, 20–34 Extension: 35, 37 ▼Exercises: 11–17, 19 Extension: 36
Assessment Guide	Mixed Review: Exercises 43–49	TE: Lesson Quiz: 10-5

RESOURCE OPTIONS

Teaching Resources	Chapter 10 Grab & Go File:
	  Practice 10-5, Reteaching 10-5
	  Enrichment 10-5
	Spanish Vocabulary Workbook and Study Skills
		All-in-One Student Workbook 10-5
		Spanish Practice Workbook 10-5

Transparencies	Check Skills You'll Need 10-5 Additional Examples 10-5 Test-Taking Strategies 10, with practice sheet	Lesson Quiz 10-5 Student Edition Answers 10-5
Technology	Interactive Textbook Online ExamView Assessment Suite Teacher Express Presentation Express with QuickTake	Worksheets Online Success Tracker Online Intervention

Lesson 10-6

Circles and Arcs

INTRODUCE

Check Skills You'll Need (p. 566)
Students review finding the diameter of a circle when given the radius, and the radius when given the diameter. Students also review finding percents of a number.

FACILITATE

Math Background (p. 566)
Discuss with students an accurate ratio used for π, as well as other not-so-accurate values.

Quick Check questions (pp. 567–569)
Assign these questions after each Example to see whether students understand the concepts presented.

Objectives
▼ Find the measures of central angles and arcs
▼ Find circumference and arc length

New Vocabulary
circle, center, radius, congruent circles, diameter, central angle, semicircle, minor arc, major arc, adjacent arcs, circumference, pi, concentric circles, arc length, congruent arcs

Standards
• NCTM Standards: Algebra, Geometry, Measurement, Data Analysis and Probability, Problem Solving, Reasoning and Proof, Communication, Connections, Representation

	Informal Geometry Course	**Optional Material**
Teaching Guide	▼ *Central Angles and Arcs* (pp. 566–568) **Example 1:** Real-World Connection **Example 2:** Identifying Arcs **Example 3:** Finding the Measures of Arcs ▼ *Circumference and Arc Length* (pp. 568–569) **Example 4:** Real-World Connection **Example 5:** Finding Arc Length TE: Additional Examples 1–5, pages 568–569	
Assignment Guide	▼ Informal Geometry Exercises: 1–26, 42–44, 49, 50 ▼ Informal Geometry Exercises: 27–39, 54–58	▼ Exercises: 40, 41, 45–48, 51–53 Extension: 70 ▼ Exercises: 59–69 Extension: 71, 72
Assessment Guide	Test Prep: Exercises 73–75 Mixed Review: Exercises 76–83 TE: Lesson Quiz: 10-6	

RESOURCE OPTIONS

Teaching Resources	Chapter 10 Grab & Go File: 　Practice 10-6, Reteaching 10-6 　Enrichment 10-6 Spanish Vocabulary Workbook and Study Skills	All-in-One Student Workbook 10-6 Spanish Practice Workbook 10-6
Transparencies	Check Skills You'll Need 10-6 Additional Examples 10-6 Test-Taking Strategies 10, with practice sheet	Lesson Quiz 10-6 Student Edition Answers 10-6
Technology	Interactive Textbook Online ExamView Assessment Suite Teacher Express Presentation Express with QuickTake	Worksheets Online Success Tracker Online Intervention

Lesson 10-7

Areas of Circles and Sectors

INTRODUCE

Check Skills You'll Need (p. 575)
Students review finding the radius, diameter, and circumference of a circle.

Hands-on Activity (p. 575)
Students cut a circle into 16 sectors and arrange the pieces to form a figure similar to a rectangle. Through algebra they develop an expression for the area of a circle.

FACILITATE

Math Background (p. 575)
Remind students that they are estimating when substituting 3.14 or $\frac{22}{7}$ for π when finding the area of a circle or sector.

Quick Check questions (pp. 576–577)
Assign these questions after each Example to see whether students understand the concepts presented.

Objectives
▼ Find the areas of circles, sectors, and segments of circles

New Vocabulary
sector of a circle, segment of a circle

Standards
• NCTM Standards: Algebra, Geometry, Measurement, Problem Solving, Reasoning and Proof, Communication, Connections, Representation

	Informal Geometry Course	Optional Material
Teaching Guide	▼ *Finding Areas of Circles and Parts of Circles* (pp. 575–577) **Example 1:** Real-World Connection **Example 2:** Finding the Area of a Sector of a Circle **Example 3:** Finding the Area of a Segment of a Circle TE: Additional Examples 1–3, page 577	*Algebra 1 Review: Dimensional Analysis* (p. 574) Activity Lab: *Technology: Exploring Area and Circumference* (p. 581)
Assignment Guide	▼ Informal Geometry Exercises: 1–21, 25, 26	▼ Exercises: 22–24, 27–34 Extension: 35–40
Assessment Guide	Test Prep: Exercises 41–43 Mixed Review: Exercises 44–48 Checkpoint Quiz 2 TE: Lesson Quiz: 10-7	

RESOURCE OPTIONS

Teaching Resources	Chapter 10 Grab & Go File: 　Practice 10-7, Reteaching 10-7 　Enrichment 10-7 Spanish Vocabulary Workbook and Study Skills	All-in-One Student Workbook 10-7 Spanish Practice Workbook 10-7
Transparencies	Check Skills You'll Need 10-7 Additional Examples 10-7 Classroom Aid, *Table of Measures* Test-Taking Strategies 10, with practice sheet	Lesson Quiz 10-7 Student Edition Answers 10-7
Technology	Interactive Textbook Online ExamView Assessment Suite Teacher Express Presentation Express with QuickTake	Worksheets Online Success Tracker Online Intervention

Lesson 10-8

Geometric Probability

ABOUT THIS LESSON

This lesson is not typically needed in an Informal Geometry Course. Check your state guidelines to see whether you should cover any of the Optional Material listed below.

Objectives

▼ Use segment and area models to find the probabilities of events

New Vocabulary

geometric probability

Standards

- NCTM Standards: Geometry, Data Analysis and Probability, Problem Solving, Reasoning and Proof, Communication, Connections, Representation

	Informal Geometry Course	Optional Material
Teaching Guide		▼ *Using Segment and Area Models* (pp. 582–584) **Example 1:** Finding Probability Using Segments **Example 2:** Real-World Connection **Example 3:** Finding Probability Using Area **Example 4:** Real-World Connection TE: Additional Examples 1–4, pages 583–584
Assignment Guide		▼ Exercises; 1–45 Extension: 46, 47
Assessment Guide	Mixed Review: Exercises 52-57	Test Prep: Exercises 48–51 TE: Lesson Quiz: 10-8 Chapter Review (pp. 589–591) Chapter Test (p. 592) Standardized Test Prep (p. 593)

RESOURCE OPTIONS

Teaching Resources	Chapter 10 Grab & Go File:
	   Practice 10-8, Reteaching 10-8
	   Enrichment 10-8
	 Alternative Assessment, Form C
	 Geometry Test Preparation
	 Spanish Vocabulary Workbook and Study Skills
		All-in-One Student Workbook 10-8
		 Spanish Practice Workbook 10-8
		 Hands-On Activities 21
		 Chapter 10 Test, Forms F and G

Transparencies	Check Skills You'll Need 10-8 Additional Examples 10-8 Test-Taking Strategies 10, with practice sheet	Lesson Quiz 10-8 Student Edition Answers 10-8
Technology	Interactive Textbook Online ExamView Assessment Suite Teacher Express Presentation Express with QuickTake	Worksheets Online Success Tracker Online Intervention Mindpoint Quiz Show

Lesson 11-1

Space Figures and Cross Sections

INTRODUCE

Check Skills You'll Need (p. 598)
Students review identifying planes of a cube that contain three given vertices.

FACILITATE

Math Background (p. 598)
Discuss with students the informal references to plane figures..

Quick Check questions (pp. 598–600)
Assign these questions after each Example to see whether students understand the concepts presented.

Objectives
▼ Recognize polyhedra and their parts
▼ Visualize cross sections of space figures

New Vocabulary
polyhedron, face, edge, vertex, cross section

Standards
• NCTM Standards: Algebra, Geometry, Problem Solving, Communication, Connections, Representation

	Informal Geometry Course	Optional Material
Teaching Guide	▼*Identifying Parts of a Polyhedron* (pp. 598–599) **Example 1:** Identifying Vertices, Edges, and Faces **Example 2:** Using Euler's Formula **Example 3:** Verifying Euler's Formula ▼*Describing Cross Sections* (p. 599) **Example 4:** Describing a Cross Section **Example 5:** Drawing a Cross Section TE: Additional Examples 1–5, pages 599–600	Extension: *Perspective Drawing* (pp. 605–606)
Assignment Guide	▼Informal Geometry Exercises: 1–12 ▼Informal Geometry Exercises: 13–19, 21–23	▼Exercises: 20, 27–37 ▼Exercises: 24–26, 39–45 Extension: 45–54
Assessment Guide	Test Prep: Exercises 55–59 Mixed Review: Exercises 60–67 TE: Lesson Quiz: 11-1	

RESOURCE OPTIONS

Teaching Resources	Chapter 11 Grab & Go File:
	    Practice 11-1, Reteaching 11-1
	    Enrichment 11-1
	Spanish Vocabulary Workbook and Study Skills
		All-in One Student Workbook 11-1
		Spanish Practice Workbook 11-1
		Hands-On Activities 28

Transparencies	Check Skills You'll Need 11-1 Additional Examples 11-1 Test-Taking Strategies 11, with practice sheet	Lesson Quiz 11-1 Student Edition Answers 11-1
Technology	Interactive Textbook Online ExamView Assessment Suite Teacher Express Presentation Express with QuickTake	Worksheets Online Success Tracker Online Intervention

Lesson 11-2

Surface Areas of Prisms and Cylinders

INTRODUCE

Check Skills You'll Need (p. 608)
Students review finding the area of a net.

FACILITATE

Math Background (p. 608)
Remind students that the area formulas from Chapter 10 are the basis of the lateral and surface area formulas in this lesson.

Quick Check questions (pp. 609–611)
Assign these questions after each Example to see whether students understand the concepts presented.

Objectives
▼ Find the surface area of a prism
▼ Find the surface area of a cylinder

New Vocabulary
prism, bases, lateral faces, altitude, height, lateral area, surface area (of a prism), right prism, oblique prism, cylinder, bases, altitude, height, lateral area, surface area (of a cylinder), right cylinder, oblique cylinder

Standards
• NCTM Standards: Algebra, Geometry, Measurement, Problem Solving, Communication, Connections, Representation

	Informal Geometry Course	Optional Material
Teaching Guide	▼ *Finding Surface Area of a Prism* (pp. 608–610) **Example 1:** Finding Surface Area of a Prism **Example 2:** Using Formulas to Find Surface Area ▼ *Finding Surface Area of a Cylinder* (pp. 610–611) **Example 3:** Finding Surface Area of a Cylinder **Example 4:** Real-World Connection TE: Additional Examples 1–4, pages 609–611	*Algebra 1 Review:* *Literal Equations* (p. 607) *Technology: Exploring* *Surface Area* (p. 616) *Guided Problem Solving,* (p. 615)
Assignment Guide	▼ Informal Geometry Exercises: 1–7, 16, 21, 23 ▼ Informal Geometry Exercises: 8–15, 22	▼ Exercises: 17, 19, 20, 24, 26 Extension: 37 ▼ Exercises: 18, 25, 27–32 Extension: 33–36
Assessment Guide	Test Prep: Exercises 38–41 Mixed Review: Exercises 42–46 TE: Lesson Quiz: 11-2	

RESOURCE OPTIONS

Teaching Resources	Chapter 11 Grab & Go File:
	   Practice 11-2, Reteaching 11-2
	   Enrichment 11-2
	Spanish Vocabulary Workbook and Study Skills
		All-in-One Student Workbook 11-2
		Spanish Practice Workbook 11-2

Transparencies	Check Skills You'll Need 11-2 Additional Examples 11-2 Classroom Aid, *3-D Shapes: Cone & Cylinder* and *3-D Shapes: Prism & Pyramid* Test-Taking Strategies 11, with practice sheet	Lesson Quiz 11-2 Student Edition Answers 11-2
Technology	Interactive Textbook Online ExamView Assessment Suite Teacher Express Presentation Express with QuickTake	Worksheets Online Success Tracker Online Intervention

Lesson 11-3

· ·

Surface Areas of Pyramids and Cones

INTRODUCE

Check Skills You'll Need (p. 617)
Students review using the Pythagorean Theorem to find the length of the hypotenuse of right triangles.

FACILITATE

Math Background (p. 617)
Discuss with students why the formulas for the lateral area of a pyramid and the lateral area of a cone are the same.

Quick Check questions (pp. 618–620)
Assign these questions after each Example to see whether students understand the concepts presented.

Objectives
▼ Find the surface area of a pyramid
▼ Find the surface area of a cone

New Vocabulary
pyramid, base, lateral faces, vertex, altitude, height, slant height, lateral area, surface area (of a pyramid), regular pyramid, cone, base, altitude, vertex, height, slant height, lateral area, surface area (of a cone), right cone

Standards
• NCTM Standards: Algebra, Geometry, Measurement, Problem Solving, Communication, Connections, Representation

	Informal Geometry Course	Optional Material
Teaching Guide	▼ *Finding Surface Area of a Pyramid* (pp. 617–618) **Example 1:** Finding Surface Area of a Pyramid **Example 2:** Real-World Connection ▼ *Finding Surface Area of a Cone* (pp. 619–620) **Example 3:** Finding Surface Area of a Cone **Example 4:** Real-World Connection TE: Additional Examples 1–4, pages 618–619	
Assignment Guide	▼ Informal Geometry Exercises: 1–7, 14–20, 27 ▼ Informal Geometry Exercises: 8–13, 21, 23–26	▼ Exercises: 22, 28, 30–34, 36 Extension: 41 ▼ Exercises: 29, 35, 37, 38, Extension: 39, 40, 42, 43
Assessment Guide	Test Prep: Exercises 44–49 Mixed Review: Exercises 50–54 Checkpoint Quiz 1 TE: Lesson Quiz: 11-3	

RESOURCE OPTIONS

Teaching Resources	Chapter 11 Grab & Go File:
	    Practice 11-3, Reteaching 11-3
	    Enrichment 11-3
	Spanish Vocabulary Workbook and Study Skills
		All-in-One Student Workbook 11-3
		Spanish Practice Workbook 11-3
		Hands-On Activities 29

Transparencies	Check Skills You'll Need 11-3 Additional Examples 11-3 Classroom Aid, *3-D Shapes: Cone & Cylinder* and *3-D Shapes: Prism & Pyramid* Test-Taking Strategies 11, with practice sheet	Lesson Quiz 11-3 Student Edition Answers 11-3
Technology	Interactive Textbook Online ExamView Assessment Suite Teacher Express Presentation Express with QuickTake	Worksheets Online Success Tracker Online Intervention

Lesson 11-4

Volumes of Prisms and Cylinders

INTRODUCE

Check Skills You'll Need (p. 624)
Students review finding the areas of circles, triangles, and rectangles.

Hands-On Activity (p. 624)
Students layer unit cubes to create prisms and find their volumes, thus discovering Theorem 11-5.

FACILITATE

Math Background (p. 624)
Discuss with students that Cavalieri's Principle is a basis for Newton's and Leibniz's contributions to calculus.

Quick Check questions (pp. 625–627)
Assign these questions after each Example to see whether students understand the concepts presented.

Objectives
▼ Find the volume of a prism
▼ Find the volume of a cylinder

New Vocabulary
volume, composite space figure

Standards
• NCTM Standards: Algebra, Geometry, Measurement, Problem Solving, Reasoning and Proof, Communication, Connections, Representation

	Informal Geometry Course	Optional Material
Teaching Guide	▼ *Finding Volume of a Prism* (pp. 624–626) **Example 1:** Finding Volume of a Rectangular Prism **Example 2:** Finding Volume of a Triangular Prism ▼ *Finding Volume of a Cylinder* (pp. 626–627) **Example 3:** Finding Volume of a Cylinder **Example 4:** Finding Volume of a Composite Figure TE: Additional Examples 1–4, pages 625–626	
Assignment Guide	▼ Informal Geometry Exercises: 1–8, 14, 18–20 ▼ Informal Geometry Exercises: 9–13, 15, 17, 23	▼ Exercises: 16, 21, 22, 24, 25, 29, 36 Extension: 39 ▼ Exercises: 26–28, 30–35 Extension: 37, 38, 40
Assessment Guide	Test Prep: Exercises 41–45 Mixed Review: Exercises 46–51 TE: Lesson Quiz: 11-4	

RESOURCE OPTIONS

Teaching Resources	Chapter 11 Grab & Go File:
	    Practice 11-4, Reteaching 11-4
	    Enrichment 11-4
	Spanish Vocabulary Workbook and Study Skills
		All-in-One Student Workbook 11-4
		Spanish Practice Workbook 11-4

Transparencies	Check Skills You'll Need 11-4 Additional Examples 11-4 Classroom Aid, *3-D Shapes: Cone & Cylinder* and *3-D Shapes: Prism & Pyramid* Test-Taking Strategies 11, with practice sheet	Lesson Quiz 11-4 Student Edition Answers 11-4
Technology	Interactive Textbook Online ExamView Assessment Suite Teacher Express Presentation Express with QuickTake	Worksheets Online Success Tracker Online Intervention

Lesson 11-5

Volumes of Pyramids and Cones

INTRODUCE

Check Skills You'll Need (p. 631)
Students review using the Pythagorean Theorem to find missing values in space figures.

Hands-On Activity (p. 631)
Students make a cube and a regular square pyramid with the same base. By pouring rice from the pyramid to the cube, they discover that the volume of a pyramid is one third the volume of a cube with the same base.

FACILITATE

Math Background (p. 631)
Explain to students how the relationship of the volumes of cylinders and cones led to the modern method of limits.

Quick Check questions (pp. 632–634)
Assign these after each Example to see whether students understand the concepts presented.

Objectives
▼ Find the volume of a pyramid
▼ Find the volume of a cone

New Vocabulary
none

Standards
- NCTM Standards: Algebra, Geometry, Measurement, Problem Solving, Reasoning and Proof, Communication, Connections, Representation

---

	Informal Geometry Course	Optional Material
Teaching Guide	▼ *Finding Volume of a Pyramid* (pp. 631–632) **Example 1:** Real-World Connection **Example 2:** Finding Volume of a Pyramid ▼ *Finding Volume of a Cone* (pp. 633–634) **Example 3:** Finding Volume of an Oblique Cone **Example 4:** Real-World Connection TE: Additional Examples 1–4, pages 632–633	
Assignment Guide	▼ Informal Geometry Exercises: 1–10, 16–18 ▼ Informal Geometry Exercises: 11–15, 22, 23	▼ Exercises: 20, 21, 24 Extension: 35 ▼ Exercises: 19, 25–30 Extension: 31–34, 36
Assessment Guide	Test Prep: Exercises 37–42 Mixed Review: Exercises 43–48 TE: Lesson Quiz: 11-5	

RESOURCE OPTIONS

Teaching Resources	Chapter 11 Grab & Go File: 　　Practice 11-5, Reteaching 11-5 　　Enrichment 11-5 Spanish Vocabulary Workbook and Study Skills	All-in-One Student Workbook 11-5 Spanish Practice Workbook 11-5
Transparencies	Check Skills You'll Need 11-5 Additional Examples 11-5 Classroom Aid, *3-D Shapes: Cone & Cylinder* and *3-D Shapes: Prism & Pyramid* Test-Taking Strategies 11, with practice sheet	Lesson Quiz 11-5 Student Edition Answers 11-5
Technology	Interactive Textbook Online ExamView Assessment Suite Teacher Express Presentation Express with QuickTake	Worksheets Online Success Tracker Online Intervention

72　Lesson 11-5

Informal Geometry Lesson Plans and Assessments

All rights reserved.

© Pearson Education, Inc., publishing as Pearson Prentice Hall.

Lesson 11-6

Surface Areas and Volumes of Spheres

INTRODUCE

Check Skills You'll Need (p. 638)
Students review finding area and circumference of circles.

FACILITATE

Math Background (p. 638)
Explain to students that Archimedes is credited with developing the formulas for the surface area and volume of a sphere.

Quick Check questions (pp. 639–640)
Assign these questions after each Example to see whether students understand the concepts presented.

Objectives
▼ Find the surface area and volume of a sphere

New Vocabulary
sphere, center, radius, diameter, circumference (of a sphere), great circle, hemisphere

Standards
• NCTM Standards: Algebra, Geometry, Measurement, Problem Solving, Communication, Connections, Representation

Teaching Guide	▼ *Finding Surface Area and Volume of a Sphere* (pp. 638–640) **Example 1:** Finding Surface Area **Example 2:** Real-World Connection **Example 3:** Finding Volume **Example 4:** Using Volume to Find Surface Area TE: Additional Examples 1–4, pages 639–640	
Assignment Guide	▼Informal Geometry Exercises: 1–23	▼Exercises: 24–44 Extension: 45–51
Assessment Guide	Test Prep: Exercises 52–59 Mixed Review: Exercises 60–67 Checkpoint Quiz 2 TE: Lesson Quiz: 11-6	

RESOURCE OPTIONS

Teaching Resources	Chapter 11 Grab & Go File: Practice 11-6, Reteaching 11-6 Enrichment 11-6 Spanish Vocabulary Workbook and Study Skills	All-in-One Student Workbook 11-6 Spanish Practice Workbook 11-6 Hands-On Activities 30
Transparencies	Check Skills You'll Need 11-6 Additional Examples 11-6 Test-Taking Strategies 11, with practice sheet	Lesson Quiz 11-6 Student Edition Answers 11-6
Technology	Interactive Textbook Online ExamView Assessment Suite Teacher Express Presentation Express with QuickTake	Worksheets Online Success Tracker Online Intervention

Lesson 11-7

Areas and Volumes of Similar Solids

ABOUT THIS LESSON

This lesson is not typically needed in an Informal Geometry Course. Check your state guidelines to see whether you should cover any of the Optional Material listed below.

Objectives
▼ Find relationships between the ratios of the areas and volumes of similar solids

New Vocabulary
similar solids, similarity ratio

Standards
- NCTM Standards: Algebra, Geometry, Measurement, Problem Solving, Communication, Connections, Representation

	Informal Geometry Course	**Optional Material**
Teaching Guide		▼*Finding Relationships in Area and Volume* (pp. 646–648) **Example 1:** Identifying Similar Solids **Example 2:** Finding the Similarity Ratio **Example 3:** Using a Similarity Ratio **Example 4:** Real-World Connection TE: Additional Examples 1–4, pages 647–648 Activity Lab: *Technology: Exploring Similar Solids* (p. 645)
Assignment Guide		▼Exercises: 1–34 Extension: 35–37
Assessment Guide	Mixed Review: Exercises 43–50	Test Prep: Exercises 38–42 TE: Lesson Quiz: 11-7 Chapter Review (pp. 653–655) Chapter Test (p. 656) Standardized Test Prep (p. 657)

RESOURCE OPTIONS

Teaching Resources	Chapter 11 Grab & Go File:
	  Practice 11-7, Reteaching 11-7
	  Enrichment 11-7
	Chapter 11 Test, Forms F and G
	Spanish Vocabulary Workbook and Study Skills
		All-in-One Student Workbook 11-7
		Spanish Practice Workbook 11-7
		Alternative Assessment, Form C
		Geometry Test Preparation

Transparencies	Check Skills You'll Need 11-7 Additional Examples 11-7 Classroom Aid, *Spreadsheet* Test-Taking Strategies 11, with practice sheet	Lesson Quiz 11-7 Student Edition Answers 11-7
Technology	Interactive Textbook Online ExamView Assessment Suite Teacher Express Presentation Express with QuickTake	Worksheets Online Success Tracker Online Intervention Mindpoint Quiz Show

Lesson 12-1

Tangent Lines

INTRODUCE

Check Skills You'll Need (p. 662)
Students review squaring a binomial and using the Pythagorean Theorem.

FACILITATE

Math Background (p. 662)
Explain to students that a tangent to a circle can be interpreted as a derivative, one of the fundamental concepts of calculus.

Quick Check questions (pp. 662–665)
Assign these after each Example to see whether students understand the concepts presented.

Objectives
▼ Use the relationship between a radius and a tangent
▼ Use the relationship between two tangents from one point

New Vocabulary
tangent to a circle, point of tangency, inscribed in, circumscribed about

Standards
• NCTM Standards: Algebra, Geometry, Problem Solving, Reasoning and Proof, Communication, Connections, Representation

	Informal Geometry Course	Optional Material
Teaching Guide	▼ *Using the Radius-Tangent Relationship* (pp. 662–664) **Example 1:** Finding Angle Measures **Example 2:** Real-World Connection **Example 3:** Finding a Tangent ▼ *Using Multiple Tangents* (p. 664–665) **Example 4:** Using Theorem 12-3 **Example 5:** Circles Inscribed in Polygons TE: Additional Examples 1–5, pages 663–664	
Assignment Guide	▼ Informal Geometry Exercises: 1–4, 6–10, 13–15, 17–19 ▼ Informal Geometry Exercises: 5, 11, 12, 16	▼ Exercises: 24–27, 29 Extension: 33 ▼ Exercises: 20–23 Extension: 34
Assessment Guide	Test Prep: Exercises 35–39 Mixed Review: Exercises 40–47 TE: Lesson Quiz: 12-1	

RESOURCE OPTIONS

Teaching Resources	Chapter 12 Grab & Go File:
	  Practice 12-1, Reteaching 12-1
	  Enrichment 12-1
	Spanish Vocabulary Workbook and Study Skills
		All-in-One Student Workbook 12-1
		Spanish Practice Workbook 12-1
		Hands-On Activities 31

Transparencies	Check Skills You'll Need 12-1 Additional Examples 12-1 Test-Taking Strategies 12, with practice sheet	Lesson Quiz 12-1 Student Edition Answers 12-1
Technology	Interactive Textbook Online ExamView Assessment Suite Teacher Express Presentation Express with QuickTake	Worksheets Online Success Tracker Online Intervention

Lesson 12-2

Chords and Arcs

INTRODUCE

Check Skills You'll Need (p. 670)
Students review the rules of 30°-60°-90° triangles and 45°-45°-90° triangles to find missing leg lengths.

FACILITATE

Math Background (p. 670)
Discuss with students how Theorem 11-8 can lead to the conclusion that any three noncollinear points determine a unique circle.

Quick Check questions (pp. 670–673)
Assign these questions after each Example to see whether students understand the concepts presented.

Objectives
▼ Use congruent chords, arcs, and central angles
▼ Recognize properties of lines through the center of a circle

New Vocabulary
chord

Standards
• NCTM Standards: Algebra, Geometry, Problem Solving, Reasoning and Proof, Communication, Representation

	Informal Geometry Course	Optional Material
Teaching Guide	▼ *Using Congruent Chords, Arcs, and Central Angles* (pp. 670–671) **Example 1:** Using Theorem 12-4 **Example 2:** Using Theorem 12-5 ▼ *Lines Through the Center of a Circle* (pp. 672–673) **Example 3:** Using Diameters and Chords TE: Additional Examples 1–3, pages 671–672	Activity Lab: *Paper Folding With Circles* (p. 669) *Guided Problem Solving* (p.677)
Assignment Guide	▼ Informal Geometry Exercises: 1–8, 17 ▼ Informal Geometry Exercises: 9–16, 18	▼ Exercises: 23, 24, 27, 29–32, 35 Extension: 38 ▼ Exercises: 19–22, 25, 26, 28, 33, 34, 36, 37 Extension: 39–41
Assessment Guide	Test Prep: Exercises 42–48 Mixed Review: Exercises 49–52 TE: Lesson Quiz: 12-2	

RESOURCE OPTIONS

Teaching Resources	Chapter 12 Grab & Go File:
	   Practice 12-2, Reteaching 12-2
	   Enrichment 12-2
	Spanish Vocabulary Workbook and Study Skills
		All-in-One Student Workbook 12-2
		Spanish Practice Workbook 12-2
		Hands-On Activities 32

Transparencies	Check Skills You'll Need 12-2 Additional Examples 12-2 Classroom Aid, *Circle with Tick Marks at Each 5°* Test-Taking Strategies 12, with practice sheet	Lesson Quiz 12-2 Student Edition Answers 12-2
Technology	Interactive Textbook Online ExamView Assessment Suite Teacher Express Presentation Express with QuickTake	Worksheets Online Success Tracker Online Intervention

Lesson 12-3

Inscribed Angles

INTRODUCE

Check Skills You'll Need (p. 678)
Students review naming arcs and angles of a given circle and finding measures of arcs.

Hands-On Activity (p. 678)
Students draw two circles and measure given arcs and angles to begin to discover Theorem 11-9 and its corollaries.

FACILITATE

Math Background (p. 678)
Explain how to use Corollary 2 to the Inscribed Angle Theorem to construct a right angle.

Quick Check questions (pp. 679–681)
Assign these after each Example to see whether students understand the concepts presented.

Objectives
▼ Find the measure of an inscribed angle
▼ Find the measure of an angle formed by a tangent and a chord

New Vocabulary
inscribed angle, intercepted arc

Standards
- NCTM Standards: Algebra, Geometry, Measurement, Problem Solving, Reasoning and Proof, Communication, Connections, Representation

---

	Informal Geometry Course	**Optional Material**
Teaching Guide	▼ *Finding the Measure of an Inscribed Angle* (pp. 678–680) **Example 1:** Using the Inscribed Angle Theorem **Example 2:** Using Corollaries to Find Angle Measures ▼ *The Angle Formed by a Tangent and a Chord* (pp. 680–681) **Example 3:** Using Theorem 12-10 TE: Additional Examples 1–3, pages 679–680	
Assignment Guide	▼ Informal Geometry Exercises: 1–14, 21, 24 ▼ Informal Geometry Exercises: 15–20	▼ Exercises: 22, 23, 25–32 34–41 Extension: 42–44 ▼ Exercises: 33 Extension: 45
Assessment Guide	Test Prep: Exercises 46–50 Mixed Review: Exercises 51–58 Checkpoint Quiz 1 TE: Lesson Quiz: 12-3	

RESOURCE OPTIONS

Teaching Resources	Chapter 12 Grab & Go File: Practice 12-3, Reteaching 12-3 Enrichment 12-3 Spanish Vocabulary Workbook and Study Skills	All-in-One Student Workbook 12-3 Spanish Practice Workbook 12-3 Hands-On Activities 33
Transparencies	Check Skills You'll Need 12-3 Additional Examples 12-3 Test-Taking Strategies 12, with practice sheet	Lesson Quiz 12-3 Student Edition Answers 12-3
Technology	Interactive Textbook Online ExamView Assessment Suite Teacher Express Presentation Express with QuickTake	Worksheets Online Success Tracker Online Intervention

Lesson 12-4

Angle Measures and Segment Lengths

ABOUT THIS LESSON

This lesson is not typically needed in an Informal Geometry Course. Check your state guidelines to see whether you should cover any of the Optional Material listed below.

Objectives

▼ Find the measures of angles formed by chords, secants, and tangents

▼ Find the lengths of segments associated with circles

New Vocabulary

secant

Standards

• NCTM Standards: Algebra, Geometry, Measurement, Problem Solving, Reasoning and Proof, Communication, Connections, Representation

	Informal Geometry Course	Optional Material
Teaching Guide		▼ *Finding Angle Measures* (pp. 687–689) **Example 1:** Finding Angle Measures **Example 2:** Real-World Connection ▼ *Finding Segment Lengths* (pp. 689–690) **Example 3:** Finding Segment Lengths **Example 4:** Real-World Connection TE: Additional Examples 1–4, pages 689–690 Activity Lab: *Technology: Exploring Chords and Secants* (p. 686) Extension: *Tangent Lines and Tangent Ratios* (p. 694)
Assignment Guide		▼ Exercises: 1–8, 17–19, 27–33 Extension: 34, 35 ▼ Exercises: 9–16, 20–26 Extension: 36, 37
Assessment Guide	Mixed Review: Exercises 43–48	Test Prep: Exercises 38–42 TE: Lesson Quiz: 12-4

RESOURCE OPTIONS

Teaching Resources	Chapter 12 Grab & Go File: Practice 12-4, Reteaching 12-4 Enrichment 12-4 Spanish Vocabulary Workbook and Study Skills	All-in-One Student Workbook 12-4 Spanish Practice Workbook 12-4
Transparencies	Check Skills You'll Need 12-4 Additional Examples 12-4 Test-Taking Strategies 12, with practice sheet	Lesson Quiz 12-4 Student Edition Answers 12-4
Technology	Interactive Textbook Online ExamView Assessment Suite Teacher Express Presentation Express with QuickTake	Worksheets Online Success Tracker Online Intervention

Lesson 12-5

....

Circles in the Coordinate Plane

INTRODUCE

Check Skills You'll Need (p. 695)
Students review finding lengths of segments in the coordinate plane.

FACILITATE

Math Background (p. 695)
Explain to students that the equation for a unit circle is a basis for derivative and integral formulas used in calculus.

Quick Check questions (pp. 695–697)
Assign these questions after each Example to see whether students understand the concepts presented.

Objectives
▼ Write an equation of a circle
▼ Find the center and radius of a circle

New Vocabulary
standard form of an equation of a circle

Standards
• NCTM Standards: Algebra, Geometry, Measurement, Problem Solving, Reasoning and Proof, Communication, Connections, Representation

	Informal Geometry Course	Optional Material
Teaching Guide	▼*Writing an Equation of a Circle* (pp. 695–696) **Example 1:** Writing the Equation of a Circle **Example 2:** Using the Center and a Point on a Circle ▼*Finding the Center and Radius of a Circle* (pp. 696–697) **Example 3:** Graphing a Circle Given Its Equation **Example 4:** Real-World Connection TE: Additional Examples 1–4, pages 696–697	
Assignment Guide	▼Informal Geometry Exercises: 1–15, 27–32 ▼Informal Geometry Exercises: 16–26, 45	▼Exercises: 33–39, 41–44, 46, 48 Extension: 63 ▼Exercises: 40, 47, 49–61 Extension: 62, 64
Assessment Guide	Test Prep: Exercises 65–69 Mixed Review: Exercises 70–81 Checkpoint Quiz 2 TE: Lesson Quiz: 12-5	

RESOURCE OPTIONS

Teaching Resources	Chapter 12 Grab & Go File:
	   Practice 12-5, Reteaching 12-5
	   Enrichment 12-5
	Spanish Vocabulary Workbook and Study Skills
		All-in-One Student Workbook 12-5
		Spanish Practice Workbook 12-5

Transparencies	Check Skills You'll Need 12-5 Additional Examples 12-5 Classroom Aid, *Coordinate Plane* Test-Taking Strategies 12, with practice sheet	Lesson Quiz 12-5 Student Edition Answers 12-5
Technology	Interactive Textbook Online ExamView Assessment Suite Teacher Express Presentation Express with QuickTake	Worksheets Online Success Tracker Online Intervention

....

Lesson 12-6

Locus: A Set of Points

ABOUT THIS LESSON

This lesson is not typically needed in an Informal Geometry Course. Check your state guidelines to see whether you should cover any of the Optional Material listed below.

Objectives
▼ Draw and describe a locus

New Vocabulary
locus

Standards
• NCTM Standards: Geometry, Problem Solving, Communication, Connections, Representation

	Informal Geometry Course	Optional Material
Teaching Guide		▼ *Drawing and Describing a Locus* (pp. 701–702) **Example 1:** Describing a Locus in a Plane **Example 2:** Drawing a Locus for Two Conditions **Example 3:** Describing a Locus in Space TE: Additional Examples 1–3, page 702
Assignment Guide		▼Exercises: 1–44 Extension: 45–50
Assessment Guide	Mixed Review: Exercises 54–61	Test Prep: Exercises 51–53 TE: Lesson Quiz: 12-6 Chapter Review (pp. 707–709) Chapter Test (p. 710) Standardized Test Prep (p. 711)

RESOURCE OPTIONS

Teaching Resources	Chapter 12 Grab & Go File:
	    Practice 12-6, Reteaching 12-6
	    Enrichment 12-6
	 Chapter 12 Test, Forms F and G
	 Final Test, Forms D and E
	 Spanish Voccabulary Workbook and Study Skills
		All-in-One Student Workbook 12-6
		 Spanish Practice Workbook 12-6
		 Alternative Assessment Form C
		 Quarter 4 Test, Forms D and E
		 Geometry Test Preparation

Transparencies	Check Skills You'll Need 12-6 Additional Examples 12-6 Test-Taking Strategies 12, with practice sheet	Lesson Quiz 12-6 Student Edition Answers 12-6
Technology	Interactive Textbook Online ExamView Assessment Suite Teacher Express Presentation Express with QuickTake	Worksheets Online Success Tracker Online Intervention Mindpoint Quiz Show

Chapter Test

Chapter 1

Form F

Describe each pattern, and find the next two terms or drawings in each sequence.

1. 1, 3, 9, 27, . . .

2. 4, 15, 24, 35, . . .

3.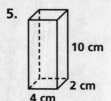

4. Critical Thinking Make a conjecture about the relationship between three consecutive whole numbers based on this relationship illustrated by the numbers 7, 8, and 9: $\frac{7+9}{2} = 8$. Can you find a counterexample?

Draw a net for each figure. Label each net with its appropriate dimensions.

5.

10 cm
2 cm
4 cm

6.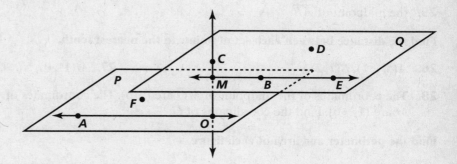

8 in.
22 in.

Use the figure to answer Exercises 7–10.

7. Name four coplanar points.

8. Name three collinear points.

9. Name four noncoplanar points.

10. Find each intersection.
  a. $\overleftrightarrow{CO}$ and plane Q
  b. $\overleftrightarrow{ME}$ and $\overleftrightarrow{CO}$
  c. plane P and point F
  d. $\overleftrightarrow{CO}$ and plane P

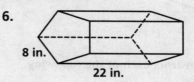

Name an angle or angles in the diagram described by each of the following.

11. supplementary to $\angle COB$

12. complementary to $\angle AOE$

13. congruent to $\angle AOD$

14. a pair of vertical angles

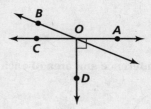

Chapter Test (continued)

Form F

Chapter 1

$2x - 1$ $9x + 3$
P   L   Q

15. Algebra $PQ = 57$. Use the figure to find each of the following.

   a. x

   b. PL

   c. LQ

Use the figure to find each measure in Exercises 16–19.

16. $m\angle ACD$

17. $m\angle DCF$

18. $m\angle FCE$

19. $m\angle ACE$

Measure and classify each angle.

20.

21.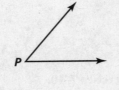

Given $\angle P$ **and** $\overline{AB}$**, construct each of the following.**

22. an angle congruent to $\angle P$

23. a segment congruent to $\overline{AB}$

24. the bisector of $\angle P$

25. the midpoint of $\overline{AB}$

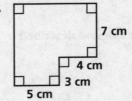

Find the distance between each set of points to the nearest tenth.

26. $A(5, -1), B(1, 2)$

27. $M(11, 0), N(-6, -3)$

28. The coordinates of the midpoint of $\overline{MG}$ are $(5, 6)$. The coordinates of M are $(1, -6)$. Find the coordinates of G.

Find the perimeter and area of each figure.

29.

21 in.

8 in.

30.

7 cm

4 cm

3 cm

5 cm

Find the circumference and area of each circle.

31.

8 in.

32.

15 cm

Chapter Test

Chapter 1

Form G

Describe each pattern, and find the next two terms or drawings in each sequence.

1. 3, 6, 12, 24, . . .

2. 8, 12, 16, 20, . . .

3.
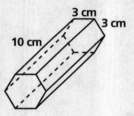

4. Critical Thinking Make a conjecture about the relationship between three consecutive even whole numbers based on this relationship illustrated by the numbers 4, 6, and 8: $\frac{4 + 8}{2} = 6$. Can you find a counterexample?

Draw a net for each figure. Label each net with its appropriate dimensions.

5.
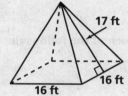

6.
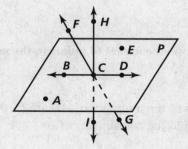

Use the figure for Exercises 7–10.

7. Name three coplanar points.

8. Name three collinear points.

9. Name four noncoplanar points.

10. Find each intersection.

    a. Name the intersection of $\overleftrightarrow{BD}$ and $\overleftrightarrow{FG}$.

    b. plane P and $\overleftrightarrow{HI}$.

Name an angle or angles in the diagram described by each of the following.

11. supplementary to $\angle LPM$

12. complementary to $\angle JPK$

13. congruent to $\angle LPK$

14. a pair of vertical angles

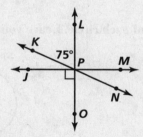

Chapter Test (continued)

Form G

Chapter 1

15. Algebra $AC = 18$. Use the figure to find each of the following.

3x + 4   2x − 1
A   B   C

    a. x

    b. AB

    c. BC

Use the figure to find each measure in Exercises 16–19.

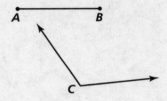

16. $m\angle QMP$

17. $m\angle LMN$

18. $m\angle PMO$

19. $m\angle LMO$

Measure and classify each angle.

20.

21.

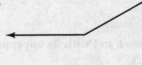

Given $\overline{AB}$ and $\angle C$, construct each of the following.

22. a segment congruent to $\overline{AB}$

23. an angle congruent to $\angle C$

24. the midpoint of $\overline{AB}$

25. the bisector of $\angle C$

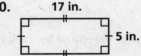

A   B

C

Find the distance between each set of points to the nearest tenth.

26. $P(6, 0), Q(-3, 0)$

27. $R(5, 7), D(-3, 6)$

28. The coordinates of the midpoint of $\overline{AB}$ are $(5, 0)$. The coordinates of A are $(7, -6)$. Find the coordinates of B.

Find the perimeter and area of each figure.

29.

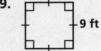

9 ft

30.

17 in.

5 in.

Find the circumference and area of each circle. Leave your answers in terms of π.

31.

5 cm

32.

14 ft

Chapter Test

Chapter 2

Form F

For each statement, (a) write the converse, and (b) decide whether the converse is true or false.

1. If a polygon is a pentagon, then it has five sides.

2. If Mary lives in Minneapolis, then she lives in Minnesota.

For Exercises 3–6, name the property that justifies each statement.

3. $AB = AB$

4. If $m\angle A = 42$ and $m\angle A = m\angle G$, then $m\angle G = 42$.

5. If $2(BC) = 13$, then $BC = 6.5$.

6. If $2(3x - 7) = x + 5$, then $6x - 14 = x + 5$.

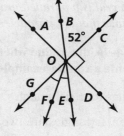

7. Use the diagram at the right to find the measure of each angle.
   a. $\angle AOB$ b. $\angle COE$
   c. $\angle FOG$ d. $\angle FOB$

For Exercises 8–10, find the value of the variable in each diagram.

8.

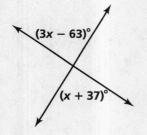

$(3x - 63)°$
$(x + 37)°$

9.

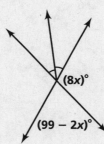

$(8x)°$
$(99 - 2x)°$

10.

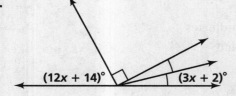

$(12x + 14)°$ $(3x + 2)°$

Chapter Test (continued)   Form F
Chapter 2

For Exercises 11–12, use deductive reasoning to draw any possible conclusions. Write *not possible* if you cannot draw any conclusions.

11. All good tennis players are quick. Martina is a good tennis player.

12. If I don't wear sunscreen while swimming, then I'll get sunburned. If I get sunburned, then I'll be in pain.

13. Rewrite the following biconditional as two conditionals:

A quadrilateral is a parallelogram if and only if it has two pairs of opposite sides that are parallel.

For Exercises 14–16, determine whether each statement is a good definition. If it is not, provide a counterexample.

14. A square has four right angles.

15. Complementary angles are two angles whose measures add up to 90.

16. Spiders have eight legs.

17. Give a reason for each step.

$5(7x + 23) = 45$ Given
$7x + 23 = 9$ **a.** _?_
$7x = -14$ **b.** _?_
$x = -2$ **c.** _?_

Find the value of *x*.

18.

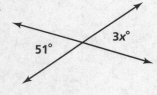

51°   3x°

19.

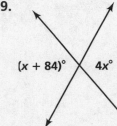

(x + 84)°   4x°

20. $\angle COF$ contains points $C(2, 4)$, $O(0, 0)$, and $F(5, 2)$. Find the coordinates of a point A so that $\overrightarrow{OA}$ is the side of an angle that is adjacent and complementary to $\angle COF$.

Chapter Test

Form G

Chapter 2

Identify the hypothesis and conclusion of each conditional.

1. If a triangle has three congruent sides, then it is equilateral.

2. If Tyler lives in San Francisco, then he lives in California.

For Exercises 3–6, name the property that justifies each statement.

3. $AB = BA$

4. If $m\angle W = m\angle A$ and $m\angle A = m\angle R$, then $m\angle W = m\angle R$

5. If $2(BC) = 24$, then $BC = 12$.

6. If $7x + 2 = 13$, then $7x = 11$.

7. Use the diagram at the right to find the measure of each angle.
   a. $\angle NOP$
   b. $\angle JPL$
   c. $\angle MPN$
   d. $\angle KJO$

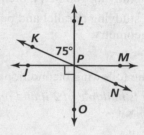

For Exercises 8–10, find the value of the variable in each diagram.

8.

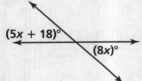

$(5x + 18)°$

$(8x)°$

9.

$(2x - 10)°$ $(6x + 14)°$

Chapter Test (continued)   Form G

Chapter 2

Use the Law of Detachment to draw a conclusion.

15. If you are at soccer practice, then you are on the soccer team.
Juan is at soccer practice.

16. If the figure is a parallelogram, it has two pairs of parallel sides.
Figure *WXYZ* is a parallelogram.

Use the Law of Syllogism to draw a conclusion.

17. If the Carson family goes camping this weekend, they will roast marshmallows.
If the weather is nice this weekend, the Carson family will go camping.

18. If you are studying geometry, then you are studying math.
If you are studying parallel and perpendicular lines, then you are studying geometry.

19. Rewrite the following biconditional as two statements:
A number is multiple of 2 if and only if it is even.

For Exercises 20–23, each conditional is true. Write its converse. If the converse is also true, combine the statements as a biconditional.

20. If two angles have the same measure, then they are congruent.

21. If a quadrilateral is a square, then it has four congruent sides.

22. If $x = 5$, then $|x| = 5$.

23. If you live in Boston, then you live in the capital of Massachusetts.

24. Give a reason for each step.

$\frac{x}{5} + 6 = 11$ Given

$\frac{x}{5} = 5$ **a.** _?_

$x = 25$ **b.** _?_

25. If $m\angle A = 145$, then what is measure of the supplement of $\angle A$?

26. If the complement of $\angle B$ is 76, then what is the measure of $\angle B$?

27. If $m\angle C = 22$, then what is the measure of the complement of $\angle C$?

Chapter Test

Chapter 3

Form F

Decide whether each statement must be *true* or *false*. Use the figure for Exercises 1–8.

1. ∠2 and ∠10 are corresponding angles.

2. ∠3 and ∠7 are alternate interior angles.

3. ∠1 and ∠8 are same-side interior angles.

4. If ∠11 and ∠15 are congruent, then $a \parallel b$.

5. If ∠14 and ∠15 are supplementary, then $c \parallel d$.

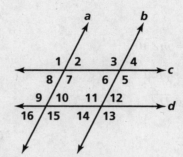

Find $m\angle 1$ and $m\angle 2$. Determine in each exercise whether ∠1 and ∠2 are alternate interior angles, same-side interior angles, or corresponding angles.

6.

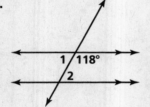

7.

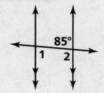

8.

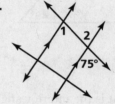

9. Graph the line $y = x - 1$. Draw the line parallel to this line that contains $(1, 2)$.

10. Graph the line $y = \frac{1}{2}x + 1$. Draw the line perpendicular to this line that contains $(-2, 1)$.

Chapter Test (continued)   Form F
Chapter 3

Use the given information to determine which segments must be parallel. If there are no such segments, write *none*.

11. $\angle 3 \cong \angle 14$

12. $m\angle 5 + m\angle 6 = m\angle 10$

13. $m\angle 4 + m\angle 14 = 180$

14. $\overline{AW} \perp \overline{WZ}$ and $\overline{DZ} \perp \overline{WZ}$

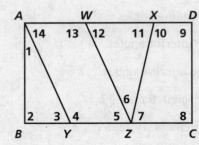

Find the values of the variables.

15.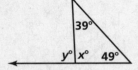

16.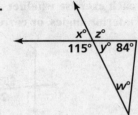

17. What is the interior angle sum of a convex decagon?

18. What is the measure of each exterior angle of a regular octagon?

Determine whether the following pairs of lines are *parallel, perpendicular,* or *neither*.

19. $y = 2x + 1$
$2x + y = 7$

20. $y = \frac{1}{3}x - 4$
$3x + y = 2$

21. $y = -4x + 1$
$4x + y = -3$

Write the equation in slope-intercept form of each line described.

22. The line is parallel to $y = 3x - 4$ and contains $(2, 5)$.

23. The line is perpendicular to $y = -4x + 1$ and contains $(8, -1)$.

24. The line has a slope of -2 and contains $(-3, 4)$.

Chapter Test

Form G

Chapter 3

Decide whether each statement must be *true* or *false*. Use the figure for Exercises 1–8.

1. ∠2 and ∠7 are alternate interior angles.

2. ∠5 and ∠6 are same-side interior angles.

3. ∠1 and ∠3 are corresponding angles.

4. If ∠14 and ∠15 are congruent, then *a* ∥ *b*.

5. If ∠10 and ∠11 are supplementary, then *c* ∥ *d*.

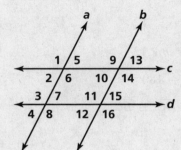

Find *m*∠1 and *m*∠2. Determine in each exercise whether ∠1 and ∠2 are alternate interior angles, same-side interior angles, or corresponding angles.

6.

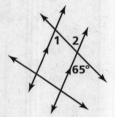

7.

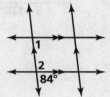

8.

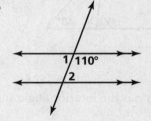

9. Graph the line $y = -x + 1$. Draw the line parallel to this line that contains $(-1, -2)$.

10. Graph the line $y = -\frac{1}{2}x - 1$. Draw the line perpendicular to this line that contains $(2, 1)$.

Chapter Test (continued)   Form G

Chapter 3

**Use the given information to determine which segments must be parallel.
If there are no such segments, write *none*.**

11. $\angle 5 \cong \angle 12$

12. $m\angle 6 + m\angle 7 = m\angle 13$

13. $m\angle 4 + m\angle 14 = 180$

14. $\overline{AB} \perp \overline{BC}$ and $\overline{DC} \perp \overline{BC}$

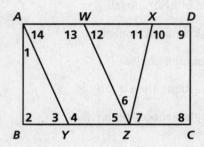

Find the values of the variables.

15.

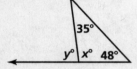

16.

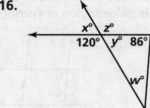

17. What is the interior angle sum of a convex octagon?

18. What is the measure of each exterior angle of a regular decagon?

**Determine whether the following pairs of lines are *parallel, perpendicular,*
or *neither*.**

19. $y = -x + 3$
$x + y = -3$

20. $y = -\frac{1}{3}x - 5$
$3x + y = 6$

21. $y = 5x + 4$
$5x + y = -8$

Write the equation in slope-intercept form of each line described.

22. The line is parallel to $y = -3x - 5$ and contains $(1, 4)$.

23. The line is perpendicular to $y = \frac{1}{2}x + 3$ and contains $(-3, 2)$.

24. The line has a slope of 2 and contains $(-2, -1)$.

Name _____ Class _____ Date _____

Chapter Test

Chapter 4

Find the values of the variables.

1.
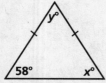

2.
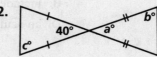

State the postulate or theorem you would use to prove each pair of triangles congruent. If the triangles cannot be proved congruent, write *not possible*.

3.
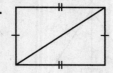

4.
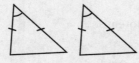

5.

6.
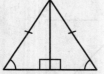

7.

8.
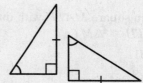

9.
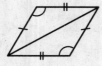

10.
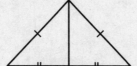

11.
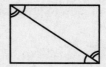

12. Draw a picture to represent $\triangle ABC \cong \triangle DEF$. Name all of the corresponding congruent parts.

Chapter Test (continued)

Form F

Chapter 4

13. When using SAS to prove triangles congruent, the angle of SAS must be

    A. a right angle.

    B. included between the two sides.

    C. a base angle.

    D. an acute angle.

$\triangle ABC \cong \triangle XYZ$. **List each of the following.**

14. three pairs of congruent sides

15. three pairs of congruent angles

16. Given $\triangle XYZ$, what is $\overline{XT}$ best described as?

    A. midpoint

    B. hypotenuse

    C. perpendicular bisector

    D. leg

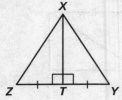

17. Given square *MATH* with diagonal $\overline{MT}$, which theorem *cannot* prove $\triangle MTH \cong \triangle MTA$?

    F. HL

    G. SSS

    H. ASA

    J. SSA

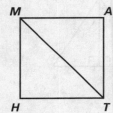

Chapter Test

Form G

Chapter 4

Find the values of the variables.

1.
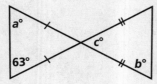

2.
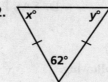

State the postulate or theorem you would use to prove each pair of triangles congruent. If the triangles cannot be proved congruent, write *not possible*.

3.
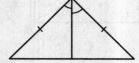

4.
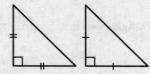

5.
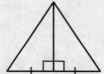

6.
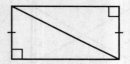

7.

8.
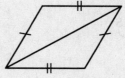

9.
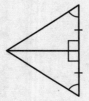

10.
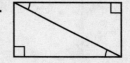

11.
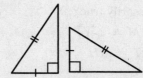

12. Draw a picture to represent $\triangle DEF \cong \triangle RST$. Name all of the pairs of corresponding congruent parts.

Chapter Test (continued)

Form G

Chapter 4

13. If $\triangle JKM \cong \triangle RST$, how do you know $\overline{JK} \cong \overline{RS}$?

    A. Definition of a line segment   **B.** SSS Postulate

    C. CPCTC   **D.** SAS Postulate

$\triangle JKL \cong \triangle PQR$. **List each of the following.**

14. three pairs of congruent angles

15. three pairs of congruent sides

16. What method could be used to find $\triangle PQR \cong \triangle RSP$ with only the given information?

    A. HL   **B.** ASA

    C. AAS   **D.** The triangles are not congruent.

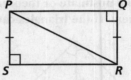

17. If $\triangle MXH \cong \triangle AXT$, which of the following statements is not necessarily true?

    A. $\angle M \cong \angle A$ **B.** $XT = MH$

    C. $AT = MH$ **D.** $\angle H \cong \angle T$

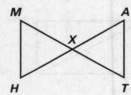

Chapter Test

Chapter 5

Form F

Find the value of *x*.

1.

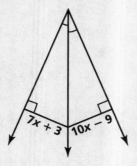

2.

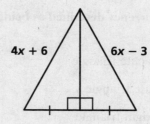

3.

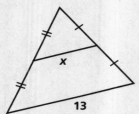

4.

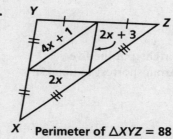

Perimeter of △XYZ = 88

5. What can you conclude about segments *VP* and *TR* from the diagram below?

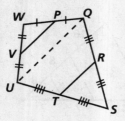

List the angles of △BCD from least to greatest.

6. $BC = 7, CD = 12, BD = 16$

7. $BC = 22, CD = 24, BD = 13$

8. Philip was making triangles with sticks. If he has a 6-in. stick and a 3-in. stick, which stick can he *not* use to form a triangle?

   A. 4-in. stick   **B.** 5-in. stick

   C. 3-in. stick   **D.** 7-in. stick

Chapter Test (continued)   Form F

Chapter 5

9. Two sides of a triangle have lengths of 9 and 12. The length of the third side can be any number between __?__ and __?__.

Classify each point of concurrency described as being *inside*, *outside*, or *on* the triangle.

10. the orthocenter of an acute triangle

11. the incenter of an obtuse triangle

12. the circumcenter of a right triangle

13. In the figure at the right, which segment is the longest?

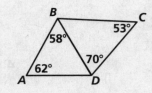

14. In the figure at the right, put the five segments in order from shortest to longest.

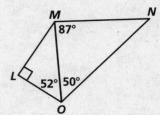

Find the value of *x*.

15.

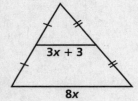

16.

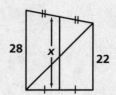

17.

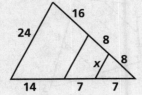

Chapter Test
Chapter 5

Find the value of x.

1.

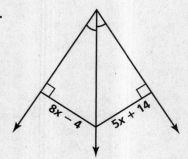

$8x - 4$ $5x + 14$

2.

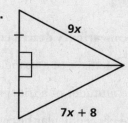

$9x$

$7x + 8$

3.

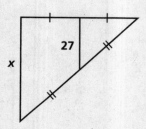

x 27

4.

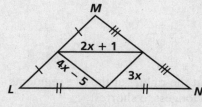

M
$2x + 1$
$4x - 5$ $3x$
L N

Perimeter of △LMN = 46

5. What can you conclude about segments *EK* and *GI* from the diagram below?

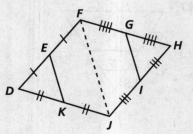

List the angles of △BCD from least to greatest.

6. $BC = 13, CD = 5, BD = 10$

7. $BC = 11, CD = 19, BD = 13$

8. During lunch, Lana was making triangles with straws. If she has a 5-in. straw and a 8-in. straw, which straw can she *not* use to form a triangle?

A. 3-in. straw   **B.** 5-in. straw

C. 6.5-in. straw   **D.** 10-in. straw

Chapter Test (continued)

Chapter 5

Form G

9. Two sides of a triangle have lengths of 6 and 11. The length of the third side can be any number between __?__ and __?__.

Give the name of each point of concurrency described.

10. the intersection of the three medians of a triangle

11. the intersection of the three altitudes of a triangle

12. the intersection of the three perpendicular bisectors of the sides of a triangle

13. In the figure at the right, which segment is the shortest?

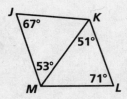

14. In the figure at the right, put the five segments in order from longest to shortest.

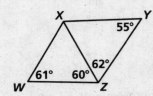

Find the value of *x*.

15.

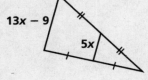

16.

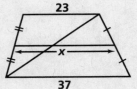

17.

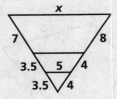

Name _____ Class _____ Date _____

Chapter Test

Chapter 6

Form F

Graph quadrilateral *ABCD*. Then determine the most precise name for each quadrilateral.

1. $A(0, 5), B(-5, 0), C(0, -5), D(5, 0)$

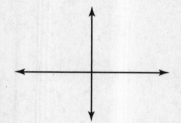

2. $A(-4, 4), B(3, 4), C(5, 0), D(-2, 0)$

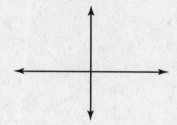

3. $A(6, 10), B(9, 8), C(6, 2), D(3, 8)$

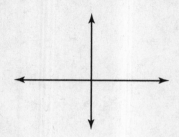

4. $A(-3, 5), B(1, 7), C(3, 2), D(-7, -3)$

Find *XY* in each parallelogram.

5.

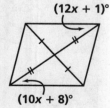

6.

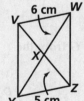

7.

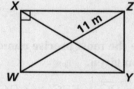

Find the values of the variables for each figure.

8.

9.

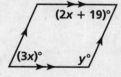

10.

$AC = 5x - 7 \quad BD = 2x + 11$

Chapter Test (continued)

Chapter 6

Find the measures of the numbered angles.

11.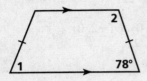

12.

13.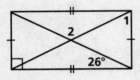

14.

15.

16.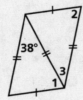

Determine the most precise name of quadrilateral *DEFG* from the information given.

17. $\overline{EF} \cong \overline{DG}$, $\angle FEG \cong \angle DGE$

18. $\overline{DE} \parallel \overline{FG}$, $\overline{DG} \parallel \overline{EF}$, $m\angle DHG = 90$

19. $\overline{DE} \perp \overline{DG}$, $\overline{GF} \perp \overline{DG}$, $m\angle DEF = 120$

20. $DE = EF = FG = DG$, $DF = EG$

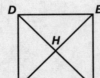

Chapter Test

(bonunoo) 3291 193qcho

Chapter 6

Form G

Graph quadrilateral *ABCD*. Then determine the most precise name for each quadrilateral.

1. $A(-4, 1), B(3, 8), C(6, 5), D(-1, -2)$

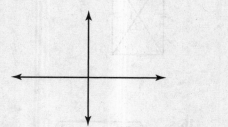

2. $A(2, 7), B(8, 5), C(2, 3), D(-4, 5)$

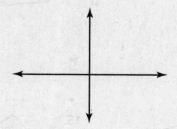

3. $AA(0, 0), B(2, 3), C(5, 1), D(3, -2)$

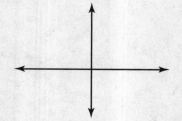

4. $A(-3, 1), B(-3, 8), C(5, 5), D(5, -2)$

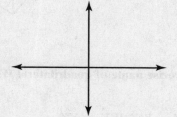

Find *AB* in each parallelogram.

5.

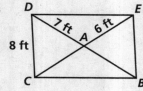

6.

7.

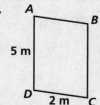

Find the values of the variables for each figure.

8.

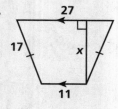

9.

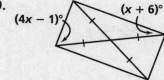

10.

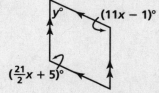

Chapter Test (continued)

Form G

Chapter 6

Find the measures of the numbered angles.

11.

12.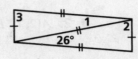

13.

14.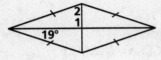

15.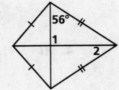

16.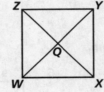

Determine the most precise name of quadrilateral *WXYZ* from the information given.

17. $WX = XY = YZ = WZ, WY = XZ$

18. $\triangle WXY \cong \triangle WZY, WZ \neq YZ$

19. $\overline{WX} \parallel \overline{ZY}, \overline{WZ} \parallel \overline{XY}, m\angle WQZ = 90$

20. $\overline{WX} \perp \overline{WZ}, \overline{ZY} \perp \overline{WZ}, m\angle WXY = 120$

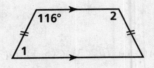

Chapter Test

Form F

Chapter 7

Solve each proportion.

1. $\frac{12}{x} = \frac{4}{7}$

2. $\frac{x}{10} = \frac{7}{20}$

3. $\frac{x}{x+5} = \frac{5}{7}$

Are the triangles similar? If so, write the similarity statement, and name the postulate or theorem that you can use to prove that they are similar. If not, write *not similar*.

4.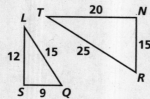

5.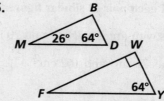

6.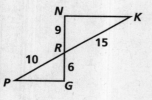

7.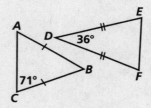

8. A person 2 m tall casts a shadow 5 m long. At the same time, a building casts a shadow 24 m long. How tall is the building?

9. Find the geometric mean of 9 and 25. If the answer is not a whole number, leave it in simplest radical form.

10. Which proportion is true for the figure to the right?

    A. $\frac{AC}{DF} = \frac{DE}{AB}$

    B. $\frac{BC}{AB} = \frac{EF}{DE}$

    C. $\frac{AD}{BE} = \frac{BE}{CF}$

    D. $\frac{AB}{EF} = \frac{DE}{EF}$

    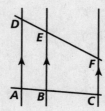

Chapter Test (continued)   **Form F**

Chapter 7

Find the value of x.

11.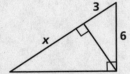

12.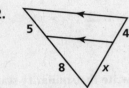

Find the similarity ratio of each pair of similar figures.

13. two regular hexagons with areas 180 in.^{2} and 20 in.^{2}

14. two squares with areas 72 cm^2 and 162 cm^2

Find the values of the variables.

15.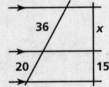

16.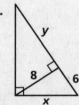

17. Find the length of the altitude to the hypotenuse of a right triangle whose sides have lengths 6, 8, and 10.

Chapter Test

Chapter 7

Solve each proportion.

1. $\frac{8}{x} = \frac{4}{11}$

2. $\frac{x}{15} = \frac{3}{20}$

3. $\frac{x}{x+3} = \frac{3}{4}$

Are the triangles similar? If so, write the similarity statement, and name the postulate or theorem that you can use to prove that they are similar. If not, write *not similar*.

4.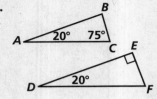

5.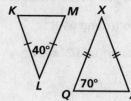

6.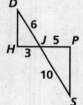

7.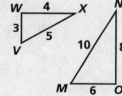

8. A person 6 ft tall casts a shadow 8 ft long. At the same time, a building casts a shadow 36 ft long. How tall is the building?

9. Find the geometric mean of 4 and 16. If the answer is not a whole number, leave it in simplest radical form.

10. Which proportion is true for the figure at the right?

    A. $\frac{RS}{MP} = \frac{RT}{MN}$ **B.** $\frac{RM}{RT} = \frac{SN}{ST}$

    C. $\frac{RT}{MP} = \frac{ST}{NP}$ **D.** $\frac{MN}{RS} = \frac{RT}{MP}$

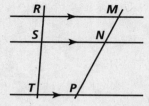

Chapter Test (continued)

Form G

Chapter 7

Find the value of *x*.

11.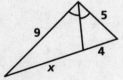

12.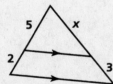

Find the similarity ratio of each pair of similar figures.

13. two triangles with areas 16 ft^2 and 64 ft^2

14. two circles with areas 75π cm^2 and 27π cm^2

Find the values of the variables.

15.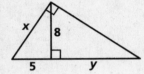

16.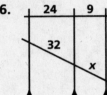

17. Find the length of the altitude to the hypotenuse of a right triangle whose sides have lengths 3, 4, and 5.

Name _____ Class _____ Date _____

Chapter Test

Chapter 8

Form F

The lengths of three sides of a triangle are given. Describe each triangle as *acute*, *right*, or *obtuse*.

1. 18, 80, 82

2. 6, 12, 16

Find the values of the variables. Leave your answers in simplest radical form.

3.

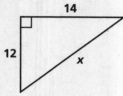

4.

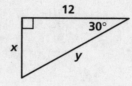

Express sin *T*, cos *T*, and tan *T* as ratios.

5.

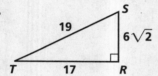

6.

Find the value of *x*. Round lengths of segments to the nearest tenth and angle measures to the nearest degree.

7.

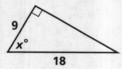

8.

9.

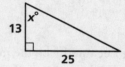

Chapter Test (continued)

Form F

Chapter 8

Find the measure of the acute angle that each line makes with a horizontal line. Round your answers to the nearest tenth.

10. $y = \frac{3}{4}x + 2$

11. $y = 5x - 10$

12. Describe each angle as it relates to the objects in the diagram.

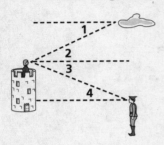

13. An airplane pilot can see the top of a traffic control tower at a 20° angle of depression. The airplane is 5000 ft from the tower. What is the altitude of the airplane?

14. **Writing** Let x and y be the measures of two acute angles of a right triangle. Explain why $\frac{\sin x°}{\cos x°} = \tan x°$. Include a diagram with your explanation.

Chapter Test

Chapter 8

Form G

The lengths of three sides of a triangle are given. Describe each triangle as *acute, right,* or *obtuse.*

1. 5, 6, 10

2. 5, 7, 9

Find the values of the variables. Leave your answers in simplest radical form.

3.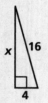

4.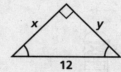

Express sin *A*, cos *A*, and tan *A* as ratios.

5.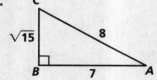

6.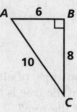

Find the value of *x.* Round lengths of segments to the nearest tenth and angle measures to the nearest degree.

7.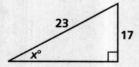

8.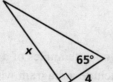

9.

Chapter Test (continued)

Form G

Chapter 8

Find the measure of the acute angle that each line makes with a horizontal line. Round your answer to the nearest tenth.

10. $y = \frac{2}{3}x + 5$

11. $y = 3x - 2$

12. Describe each angle as it relates to the objects in the diagram.

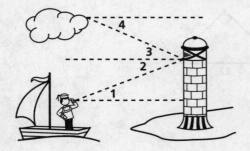

13. A tree casts a shadow of 17 ft. The angle of elevation from the tip of the shadow to the top of the tree is 68°. To the nearest foot, what is the height of the tree?

14. **Writing** Let x and y be the measures of two acute angles of a right triangle. Explain why $\frac{\cos x°}{\sin x°}(\tan x°) = 1$. Include a diagram with your explanation.

Name _____ Class _____ Date _____

Chapter Test
Chapter 9

Form F

State whether the transformation appears to be an isometry. Explain.

1.

2.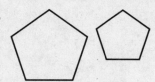

3.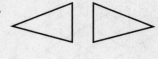

Describe each translation as a transformation rule.

4. 6 units to the left, 1 unit up

5. 3 units to the right, 7 units down

Find the coordinates of the vertices of the image of *ABCD* for each transformation.

6. reflection across *x*-axis

7. reflection across $x = 3$

8. translation $(x, y) \rightarrow (x + 3, y + 5)$

9. translation $(x, y) \rightarrow (x + 5, y - 1)$

10. rotation of 90° counter-clockwise about the point $(0, 0)$

11. rotation of 180° about point *A*

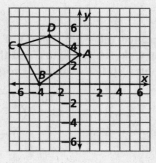

Write a rule to describe each translation.

12.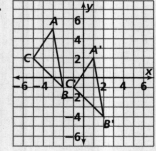

13.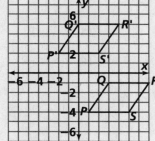

Chapter 9

14. Identify the repeating figures and a transformation in the tessellation.

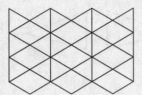

Copy △ABC and point P. Then draw the image of △ABC for the given composition of rotations about point P.

15. 60°, then 30°   **16.** 40°, then 140°

Judging from appearance, tell what type(s) of symmetry each figure has. If it has line symmetry, sketch the figure and the line(s) of symmetry. If it has rotational symmetry, state the angle of rotation.

17.   **18.**   **19.**

Find the image of each point under a 90° counter-clockwise rotation about the origin.

20. (0, 7)   **21.** (−3, 0)   **22.** (1, 6)

23. (−4, 9)   **24.** (−2, −2)   **25.** (11, 5)

Name _____ Class _____ Date _____

Chapter Test
Chapter 9

Form G

State whether the transformation appears to be an isometry. Explain.

1.

2.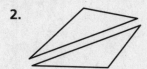

3.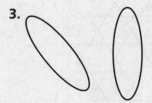

Describe each translation, using an ordered pair.

4. 3 units to the left, 4 units down

5. 10 units to the right, 5 units up

Find the coordinates of the vertices of the image of *ABCD* for each transformation.

6. reflection in *y*-axis

7. reflection in *y* = 2

8. translation ⟨3, 4⟩

9. translation ⟨−5, 2⟩

10. rotation of 180° about the point (0, 0)

11. rotation of 90° counter-clockwise about point *A*

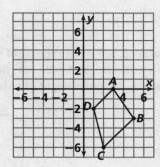

Write a rule to describe each translation.

12.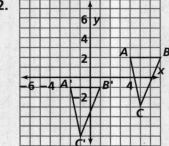

13.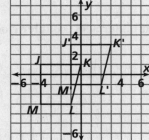

Chapter Test (continued)

Form G

Chapter 9

14. Identify the repeating figures and a transformation in the tessellation.

Copy △ABC and point P. Then draw the image of △ABC for the given composition of rotations about point P.

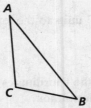

15. 45°, then 45°

16. 120°, then 60°

Judging from appearance, tell what type(s) of symmetry each figure has. If it has line symmetry, sketch the figure and the line(s) of symmetry. If it has rotational symmetry, state the angle of rotation.

17.

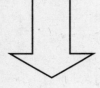

18.

19.

Find the image of each point under a 90° counter-clockwise rotation about the origin.

20. (3, 0)

21. (0, −5)

22. (−2, −7)

23. (8, 11)

24. (−3, −4)

25. (6, −1)

Chapter Test

Form F

Chapter 10

Find the area of each figure described or shown. If your answer is not an integer, round to the nearest tenth.

1. equilateral triangle with side length of 16 ft

2. regular octagon with side length of 11.6 cm and apothem of 14 cm

3. isosceles triangle with legs each 9 ft long and base 12 ft long

4.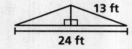

5.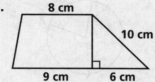

6.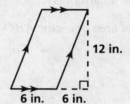

For each pair of similar figures, find the ratio of the area of the first figure to the area of the second.

7.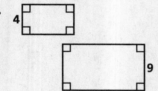

8.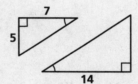

9. $\triangle ABC \sim \triangle LMN$ and $AB = \frac{3}{4}LM$. Which of the following is true?

   A. The ratio of areas of $\triangle ABC$ to $\triangle LMN$ is $\frac{9}{16}$.

   B. $m\angle C = \frac{3}{4}m\angle N$

   C. The ratio of perimeters of $\triangle LMN$ to $\triangle ABC$ is $\frac{3}{4}$.

   D. none of these

Find the area of each polygon. Round your answers to the nearest tenth.

10.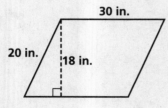

11.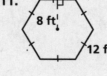

For Exercises 12–15, leave your answers in terms of π.

12. Find the circumference of $\odot O$.

13. Find the area of $\odot O$.

14. Find the length of $\overset{\frown}{CA}$.

15. Find the area of sector ABC.

16. Find the area of the shaded sector to the nearest tenth.

17. A circle has circumference 24π cm. What is its area in terms of π?

18. A circle has diameter 8 in. What is the area in terms of π of a sector of the circle with a 90° central angle?of 64π mm.

Chapter Test

Form G

Chapter 10

Find the area of each figure described or shown. If your answer is not an integer, round to the nearest tenth.

1. equilateral triangle with side length of 26 ft

2. regular hexagon with side length of 24 cm and apothem length of 19 cm

3. isosceles triangle with legs each 12 ft long and base 18 ft long

4.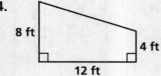

5.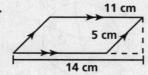

6.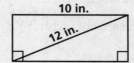

For each pair of similar figures, find the ratio of the area of the first figure to the area of the second.

7.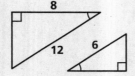

8.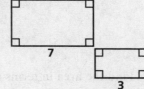

9. $\triangle JKL \sim \triangle PQR$ and $KL = \frac{2}{5}QR$. Which of the following is true?

   A. The ratio of areas of $\triangle JKL$ to $\triangle PQR$ is $\frac{25}{4}$.

   B. $m\angle K = \frac{2}{5}m\angle Q$

   C. The ratio of perimeters of $\triangle PQR$ to $\triangle JKL$ is $\frac{5}{2}$.

   D. none of these

Find the area of each polygon. Round your answers to the nearest tenth.

10.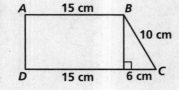

11.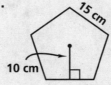

Chapter Test (continued)

Form G

Chapter 10

For Exercises 12–15, leave your answers in terms of π.

12. Find the circumference of ⊙O.

13. Find the area of ⊙O.

14. Find the length of $\overset{\frown}{XZ}$.

15. Find the area of sector *XYZ*.

16. Find the area of the shaded segment to the nearest hundredth.

17. A circle has radius 6 cm. Find the area in terms of π of a sector of the circle with a 140° central angle.

18. A circle has circumference 42π ft. Find its area in terms of π.

Chapter Test

Chapter 11

Form F

Draw a net for each figure. Label each net with its appropriate dimensions.

1.

10 cm
2 cm
4 cm

2.
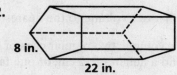

8 in.
22 in.

3. Paint roller A has a length of 11 in. and a diameter of 2 in. Paint roller
   B has a length of 7 in. and a diameter of 3 in. Which roller can spread
   more paint on a wall in one revolution? Explain, and give your
   calculations.

A.
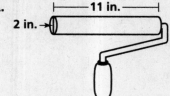

11 in.
2 in. →

B.
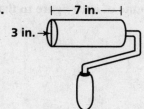

7 in.
3 in. →

Find the volume and surface area of each figure to the nearest tenth.

4.

5 m

5.
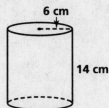

6 cm
14 cm

6.
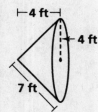

4 ft
4 ft
7 ft

7.
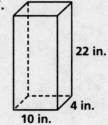

22 in.
4 in.
10 in.

Chapter Test (continued)

Chapter 11

Form F

8. **a.** What space figures can you use to approximate the shape of the ice cream cone?

   b. Find the entire figure's volume to the nearest tenth.

9. Which has a greater volume: two regular cans of soup, each with a diameter of 7 cm and a height of 12 cm, or one family-size can of soup, which has a diameter of 10 cm and a height of 12 cm? Explain and give your calculations.

10. Two similar cylinders have heights of 3 cm and 4 cm. What is the ratio of their volumes?

   A. $\frac{1}{8}$ **B.** $\frac{3}{4}$ **C.** $\frac{9}{16}$ **D.** $\frac{27}{64}$

Find the surface area and volume of each figure to the nearest tenth.

11.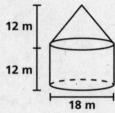

12.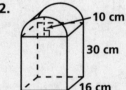

Chapter Test

Form G

Chapter 11

Draw a net for each figure. Label each net with its appropriate dimensions.

1.

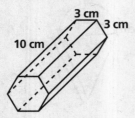

3 cm
3 cm
10 cm

2.

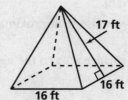

17 ft
16 ft
16 ft

3. Paint roller A has a length of 6 in.
and a radius of 2 in. Paint roller B
has a length of 9 in. and a radius of 1 in.
Which roller can spread more paint on
a wall in one revolution? Explain, and give your calculations.

A.

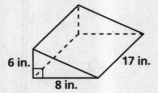

6 in.
2 in.

B.

9 in.
1 in.

Find the volume and surface area of each figure to the nearest tenth.

4.

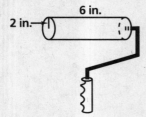

6 in.
17 in.
8 in.

5.

5 m

6.

7 cm
4 cm
11 cm

7.

15 ft
9 ft

Chapter Test (continued)

Chapter 11

8. Refer to the figure at the right.

   a. What space figures can you use to approximate the shape of the ice-cream cone?

   b. Find the entire figure's surface area to the nearest tenth.

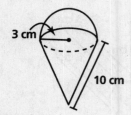

9. Which has a greater volume: two regular cans of soup, each with a diameter of 6 cm and a height of 5 cm, or one family-size can of soup, which has a diameter of 8 cm and a height of 6 cm? Explain and give your calculations.

10. Two similar cylinders have heights of 3 cm and 4 cm. What is the ratio of their volumes?

   A. $\frac{1}{8}$ B. $\frac{3}{4}$ C. $\frac{9}{16}$ D. $\frac{27}{64}$

Find the surface area and volume of each figure to the nearest tenth.

11.

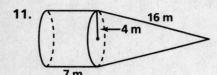

12.

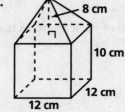

Chapter Test

Test (continued)

Form F

Chapter 12

Tell whether each polygon is inscribed in or circumscribed about the circle.

1.

2.

Identify the inscribed angle and its intercepted arc.

3.

4.

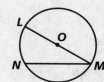

Find the center and radius of each circle.

5. $x^2 + y^2 = 25$

6. $(x - 3)^2 + (y - 5)^2 = 100$

Write the equation of each circle.

7.

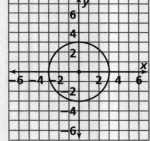

8.

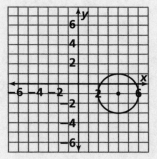

9. Find the circumference and area of the circle whose equation is $x^2 + y^2 = 36$. Round your answer to the nearest tenth.

10. Write an equation of the circle that passes through $(4, 2)$ with center $(0, -1)$.

11. Graph the circle $(x + 3)^2 + (y - 2)^2 = 9$. State the center and radius of the circle.

12. In the figure at the right, a triangle is inscribed in the circle. Find the value of x.

Chapter Test (continued)

Form F

Chapter 12

Find $m\widehat{AB}$ to the nearest whole number.

13.

14.

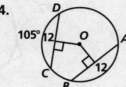

Find each indicated measure for $\odot P$.

15. $m\widehat{AC}$

16. $m\angle C$

17. $m\angle A$

18. $m\widehat{CAB}$

19. $m\widehat{ACB}$

Name _____ Class _____ Date _____

Chapter Test

Form G

Chapter 12

Tell whether each polygon is inscribed in or circumscribed about the circle.

1.

2.

Identify the inscribed angle and its intercepted arc.

3.

4.

Find the center and radius of each circle.

5. $x^2 + y^2 = 16$

6. $(x - 6)^2 + (y - 1)^2 = 81$

Write the equation of each circle.

7.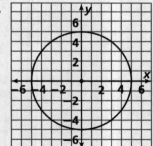

8.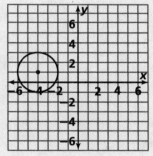

9. Find the circumference and area of the circle whose equation is $x^2 + y^2 = 64$. Round your answer to the nearest tenth.

10. Write an equation of the circle that passes through $(4, 0)$ with center $(-2, 2)$.

11. Graph the circle $(x - 1)^2 + (y + 5)^2 = 4$. State the center and radius of the circle.

12. In the figure at the right, a triangle is inscribed in the circle. Find the value of *x*.

Chapter Test (continued)

Form G

Chapter 12

Find *m$\widehat{AB}$* to the nearest whole number.

13.

14.

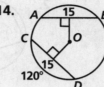

Find each indicated measure for ⊙*P*.

15. *m$\widehat{AB}$*

16. *m∠B*

17. *m∠A*

18. *m$\widehat{BC}$*

19. *m$\widehat{ABC}$*

Quarter 1 Test

Form D

Chapters 1–3

1. Find the next two terms in the sequence.

$1, 5, 9, 13, 17, \ldots$

2. Classify the triangle by its angles.

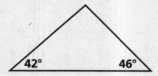

3. What is the area of a circle with diameter 12 m?

4. Find the slope of a line that contains $(3, 6)$ and $(1, 2)$.

A. 2   **B.** 3

C. $\frac{1}{2}$ **D.** -2

5. Find the value of x if $AC = 20$.

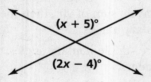

6. Find the value of x.

7. Create a foundation drawing from the isometric drawing.

8. Find $m\angle 1$.

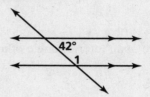

9. Find the perimeter of the polygon.

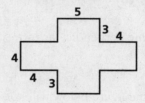

10. Which is the correct net for the figure shown?

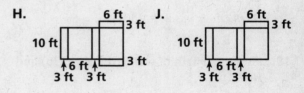

F. 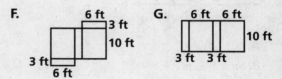 **G.**

H. **J.**

11. The length of one side of a regular octagon is 5 cm. What is the perimeter of the octagon?

12. What is the intersection of planes $ABFE$ and $BCGF$?

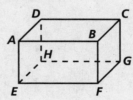

Quarter 1 Test (continued)   **Form D**

Chapters 1–3

13. Find the circumference of a circle with area 25π m^2.

14. What is the measure of an interior angle of a regular hexagon?

15. Find the coordinates of the midpoint of $(2, 3)$ and $(-6, 5)$.

16. Find the slope of a line perpendicular to $2x + y = -8$.

17. What conditions in the figure below will *not* prove $a \parallel b$?

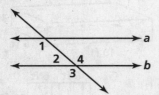

  A. $\angle 1 \cong \angle 3$

  B. $m\angle 2 + m\angle 4 = 180$

  C. $\angle 1 \cong \angle 4$

  D. $m\angle 1 + m\angle 2 = 180$

18. Find the length of $\overline{AB}$, given $A(-1, 6)$ and $B(3, 3)$.

19. Find the value of m in the regular octagon.

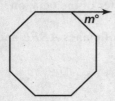

Use the figure for Exercises 20–22.

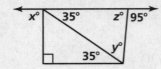

20. Find the value of x.

21. Find the value of y.

22. Find the value of z.

23. Identify the hypothesis and conclusion of the conditional.

If two angles have a sum of 180°, then they are supplementary angles.

24. Which of the following is the converse of the conditional in Exercise 23?

  F. If two angles have a sum of 180°, then they are same-side interior angles.

  G. If two angles are supplementary angles, then they have a sum of 180°.

  H. If two angles have a sum of 90°, then they are complementary angles.

  J. If two angles are supplementary angles, then they are congruent.

25. Name the property that justifies the following statement:

If $6x - 5 = y$ and $y = 3x - 4$, then $6x - 5 = 3x - 4$.

  A. Reflexive Property of Equality

  B. Substitution Property of Equality

  C. Symmetric Property of Equality

  D. Transitive Property of Equality

Quarter 1 Test

Form E

Chapters 1–3

1. Find the next two terms in the sequence.

1, 6, 11, 16, 21, . . .

2. Classify the triangle by its sides.

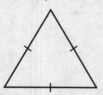

3. What is the area of a circle with diameter 20 m?

4. Find the value of x if $AC = 35$.

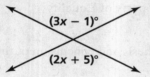

$$A \overset{(3x-6)}{\underset{B}{\bullet}} \overset{(5x+1)}{\underset{C}{\bullet}}$$

5. Find the value of x.

$(3x - 1)°$

$(2x + 5)°$

6. Create a foundation drawing from the isometric drawing.

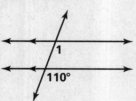

Front   Right

7. Find $m\angle 1$.

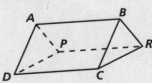

1

110°

8. Find the perimeter of the polygon.

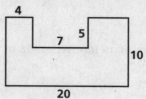

4

7   5

10

20

9. Which is the correct net for the figure shown?

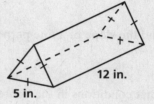

12 in.

5 in.

A. 12 in.   5 in.

B. 12 in.   5 in.   5 in.

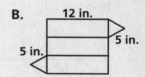

C. 12 in.   5 in.   5 in.

D. 12 in.   5 in.   5 in.

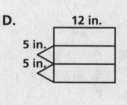

10. Find the slope of a line that contains $(2, 5)$ and $(1, 2)$.

F. $\frac{1}{3}$ **G.** 3

H. $-\frac{1}{3}$ **J.** -3

11. The length of one side of a regular hexagon is 10 in. What is the perimeter of the hexagon?

12. What is the intersection of planes $ABCD$ and $ABRP$?

A   B

P   R

D   C

13. Find the circumference of a circle with area 49π m^2.

14. What is the measure of an interior angle of a regular octagon?

15. Find the coordinates of the midpoint of $(-3, 7)$ and $(5, 3)$.

16. Find the slope of a line perpendicular to $3x - y = -5$.

17. What conditions in the figure below will *not* prove $m \parallel n$?

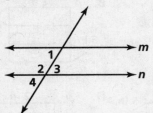

A. $\angle 1 \cong \angle 3$

B. $m\angle 1 + m\angle 2 = 180$

C. $\angle 1 \cong \angle 4$

D. $m\angle 2 + m\angle 3 = 180$

18. Find the length of $\overline{AB}$, given $A(5, 1)$ and $B(-1, 9)$.

19. Find the value of m in the regular pentagon.

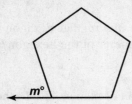

Use the figure for Exercises 20–22.

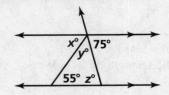

20. Find the value of x.

21. Find the value of y.

22. Find the value of z.

23. Name the property that justifies the following statement:

If $3y - 7 = 5$, then $3y = 12$.

F. Symmetric Property of Equality

G. Addition Property of Equality

H. Substitution Property of Equality

J. Subtraction Property of Equality

24. Identify the hypothesis and conclusion of the conditional.

If two lines form right angles, then the lines are perpendicular.

25. Which of the following is the converse of the conditional in Exercise 24?

A. If two lines are perpendicular, then their angles are supplementary.

B. If two lines form right angles, then the lines intersect.

C. If two lines are perpendicular, then they form right angles.

D. If two lines form right angles, then the lines are parallel

Quarter 2 Test

~~2 Test (continued)~~

Form D

Chapters 4–6

1. $\triangle ABC \cong \triangle XYZ$. What side is congruent to $\overline{AC}$?

2. Find the value of x.

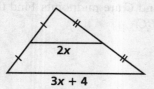

3. What is the most precise name for a quadrilateral with four right angles and four congruent sides?

   A. parallelogram   **B.** rectangle

   C. rhombus   **D.** square

4. An isosceles triangle has two angles measuring 55 and 70. What is the measure of the third angle?

5. Find the values of x and y.

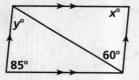

6. What term best identifies $\overline{AX}$?

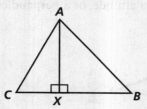

   F. altitude   **G.** median

   H. midpoint   **J.** perpendicular bisector

7. List the angles of $\triangle ABC$ from smallest to largest if $AB = 12$, $BC = 16$, and $AC = 22$.

8. $QRST$ is a rhombus, and $m\angle S = 71$. Find $m\angle 1$, $m\angle 2$, and $m\angle 3$.

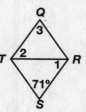

For Exercises 9–12, choose the correct letter of the postulate or theorem that can be used to prove each pair of triangles congruent.

   A. AAS   **B.** ASA   **C.** HL

   D. SAS   **E.** SSS

9.

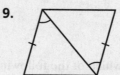

10.

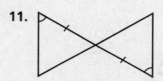

11.

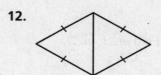

12.

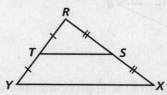

13. Find the perimeter of $\triangle RST$.

$RX = 40$

$YT = 10$

$XY = 50$

Quarter 2 Test (continued)

Form D

Chapters 4–6

14. Find $m\angle YXZ$.

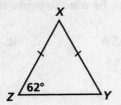

15. If $\triangle PRS \cong \triangle XYZ$, then which of the following is not true?

F. $\angle PRS \cong \angle XYZ$ **G.** $\overline{PS} \cong \overline{XZ}$

H. $\angle RSP \cong \angle YXZ$ **J.** $\overline{ZX} \cong \overline{SP}$

16. Find the measures of the numbered angles for parallelogram *MATH*.

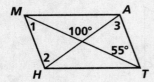

17. *ABCD* is a rhombus. Find $m\angle 1, m\angle 2$, and $m\angle 3$.

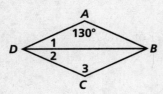

18. Fill in the blank with the appropriate choice.

The bisectors of the angles of a triangle are __?__ at a point equidistant from the sides.

A. concurrent   **B.** congruent

C. parallel   **D.** perpendicular

19. List the names of all the quadrilaterals that have two pairs of opposite parallel sides.

20. In $\triangle XYZ$, *A*, *B*, and *C* are midpoints. Find the perimeter of $\triangle ABC$.

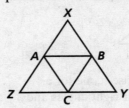

$XY = 118$

$YZ = 110$

$XZ = 100$

21. Which two angles must be congruent to use SAS to prove $\triangle ADX \cong \triangle CBX$?

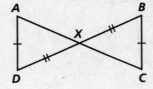

22. Is $\overline{XZ}$ a median, an altitude, or a perpendicular bisector?

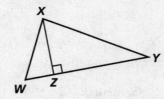

23. Given rectangle *ABCD*, find the perimeter of $\triangle WDC$.

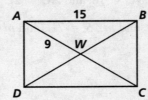

Quarter 2 Test

Form E

Chapters 4–6

1. $\triangle AMR \cong \triangle PST$. What angle is congruent to $\angle T$?

2. Find the value of x.

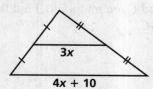

3. What is the most precise name for a quadrilateral with four congruent sides?

   A. parallelogram **B.** rectangle

   C. rhombus **D.** square

4. An isosceles triangle has a base angle of 65. What are the measures of the other two angles?

5. Find the values of x and y.

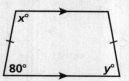

6. What term best identifies $\overline{XZ}$?

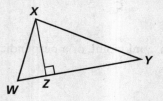

   F. altitude **G.** median

   H. midpoint **J.** perpendicular bisector

7. List the angles of $\triangle ABC$ from smallest to largest if $AB = 18$, $BC = 24$, and $AC = 22$.

8. $BDST$ is a rhombus, and $m\angle B = 122$. Find $m\angle 1$, $m\angle 2$, and $m\angle 3$.

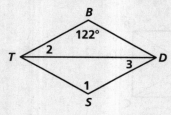

For Exercises 9–12, choose the correct letter of the postulate or theorem that can be used to prove each pair of triangles congruent.

   A. AAS **B.** ASA **C.** HL

   D. SAS **E.** SSS

9.

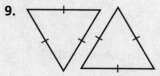

10.

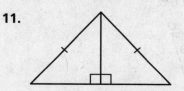

11.

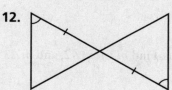

12.

13. Find the perimeter of $\triangle DMR$.

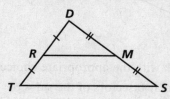

$DS = 50$

$RT = 18$

$ST = 70$

Quarter 2 Test (continued)   Form E

Chapters 4–6

14. Find $m\angle ACB$.

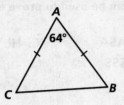

15. If $\triangle EKN \cong \triangle ADR$, then which of the following is *not* true?

  F. $\angle EKN \cong \angle ADR$ **G.** $\overline{NE} \cong \overline{DR}$

  H. $\angle KNE \cong \angle DRA$ **J.** $\overline{KE} \cong \overline{DA}$

16. Find the measures of the numbered angles for parallelogram *TOPS*.

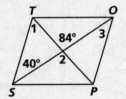

17. *PQRS* is a rhombus. Find $m\angle 1, m\angle 2$, and $m\angle 3$.

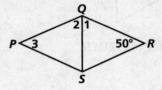

18. Fill in the blank with the appropriate choice.

The perpendicular bisectors of the sides of a triangle are __?__ at a point equidistant from the vertices.

  A. congruent   **B.** perpendicular

  C. parallel   **D.** concurrent

19. List the names of all the quadrilaterals that have supplementary consecutive angles.

20. In $\triangle XYZ$, *A*, *B*, and *C* are midpoints. Find the perimeter of $\triangle ABC$.

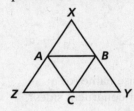

$XY = 120$

$YZ = 128$

$XZ = 126$

21. Which two sides must be congruent to use ASA to prove $\triangle ADX \cong \triangle CBX$?

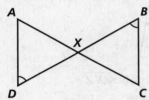

22. Is $\overline{AX}$ a median, a midpoint, or a perpendicular bisector?

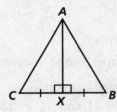

23. Given rectangle *ABCD*, find the perimeter of $\triangle ABW$.

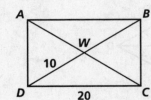

Quarter 3 Test

Chapters 7–9

Form D

Determine whether the triangles are similar. If so, write the similarity statement, and name the postulate or theorem you can use to prove they are similar.

1.

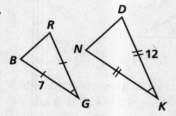

2.

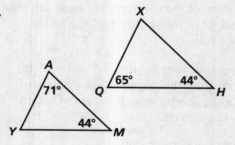

Find the value of *x*. Round your answers to the nearest tenth.

3.

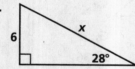

4.

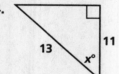

5.

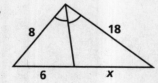

6. Choose the correct value for *x* in the proportion.

$$\frac{5}{17} = \frac{15}{x}$$

   A. 6.4   **B.** 34
   C. 250   **D.** 51

7. Find the geometric mean of 4 and 20. If your answer is not a whole number, leave it in simplest radical form.

8. Express sin *A*, cos *A*, and tan *A* as ratios.

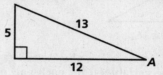

9. What is the image of $(7, 2)$ under the translation $(x, y) \rightarrow (x + 3, y - 2)$?

10. What type of symmetry does the letter have?

   F. point symmetry   **G.** line symmetry
   H. rotational symmetry   **J.** no symmetry

11. Two figures have a similarity ratio of 3 : 4. The area of the smaller figure is 63 in.^{2} What is the area of the larger figure?

12. Which transformation is illustrated in the figure shown?

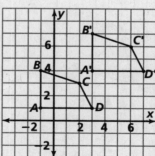

   A. translation
   B. reflection
   C. rotation
   D. glide reflection

13. Find the value of *x*. Leave your answer in simplest radical form.

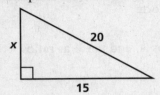

Find the values of the variable(s) for each pair of similar figures.

14.

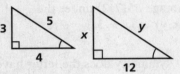

15.

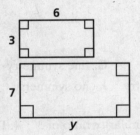

Find the coordinates of the vertices of △XYZ for each transformation.

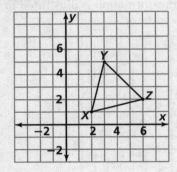

16. translation $(x, y) \rightarrow (x + 2, y + 5)$

17. reflection across *x*-axis

18. rotation of 180° about the point $(0, 0)$

19. Find the value of *x*. Leave your answer in simplest radical form.

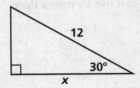

20. Two buildings are 180 ft apart. The height of the taller building is 120 ft. The angle of depression from the top of the taller building to the top of the shorter building is 10°. Find the height of the shorter building to the nearest foot.

21. A photographic negative is 1 in. by 1.5 in. A print from this negative has a length of 8 in. as its shorter side. What is the length of its longer side?

22. Choose the correct value for *x*.

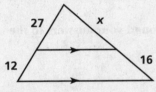

F. 20.25   **G.** 32

H. 34   **J.** 36

Name _____ Class _____ Date _____

Quarter 3 Test

Chapters 7–9

Form E

Determine whether the triangles are similar. If so, write the similarity statement, and name the postulate or theorem you can use to prove they are similar.

1.
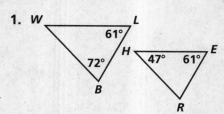

2.
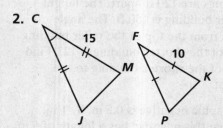

Find the value of x. Round your answers to the nearest tenth.

3.
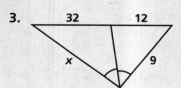

4.
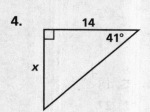

5.
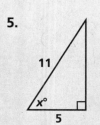

6. Choose the correct value for *x* in the proportion.

$$\frac{4}{18} = \frac{10}{x}$$

A. 40   **B.** 7

C. 45   **D.** 48

7. Find the geometric mean of 6 and 18. If your answer is not a whole number, leave it in simplest radical form.

8. Express sin *A*, cos *A*, and tan *A* as ratios.

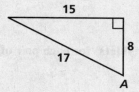

9. What is the image of $(-5, 3)$ under the translation $(x, y) \rightarrow (x - 1, y + 6)$?

10. What type of symmetry does the letter have?

F. point symmetry   **G.** line symmetry

H. rotational symmetry   **J.** no symmetry

11. Two figures have a similarity ratio of 2 : 7. The area of the smaller figure is 48 in.² What is the area of the larger figure?

12. Which transformation is illustrated in the figure shown?

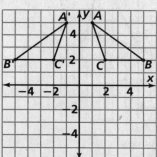

A. reflection

B. rotation

C. translation

D. glide reflection

• •

Informal Geometry Lesson Plans and Assessments   Quarter 3 Test   **139**

Quarter 3 Test (continued)   Form E

Chapters 7–9

13. Find the value of *x*. Leave your answer in simplest radical form.

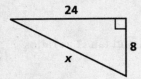

Find the values of the variable(s) for each pair of similar figures.

14.

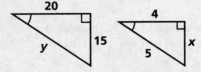

15.

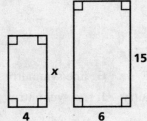

Find the coordinates of the vertices of △ABC for each transformation.

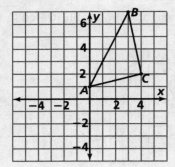

16. reflection across *y*-axis

17. translation $(x, y) \rightarrow (x + 4, y - 3)$

18. rotation of 90° about the point $(0, 0)$

19. Find the value of *x*. Leave your answer in simplest radical form.

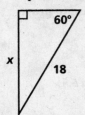

20. Two buildings are 120 ft apart. The height of the taller building is 150 ft. The angle of depression from the top of the taller building to the top of the shorter building is 12°. Find the height of the shorter building to the nearest foot.

21. A photographic negative is 0.5 in. by 1 in. A print from this negative has a length of 6 in. as its longer side. What is the length of its shorter side?

22. Choose the correct value for *x*.

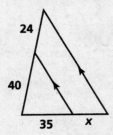

F. 21   **G.** 18

H. 12   **J.** 27

Quarter 4 Test Form D

Chapters 10–12

1. Find the volume of the sphere to the nearest tenth.

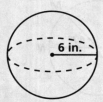

2. Two similar pentagons have corresponding sides in the ratio 4 : 7. Give the ratio of the perimeters and the ratio of the areas.

Find the value of *x*.

3.

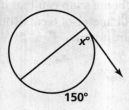

4.

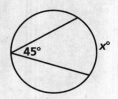

5. What is the measure of an interior angle of a regular octagon?

A. 45   **B.** 135

C. 120   **D.** 225

6. Find the area of the parallelogram.

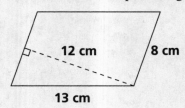

7. Find the value of *x*.

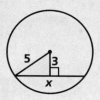

8. Find the surface area of the cylinder. Round your answer to the nearest tenth.

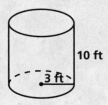

9. Find the area of the trapezoid.

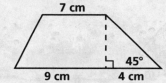

Use the figure for Exercises 10 and 11.

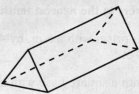

10. How many faces does the figure have?

11. How many edges does the figure have?

Quarter 4 Test (continued)

Form D

Find $m\widehat{AB}$.

12.

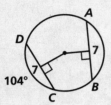

13.

14. Find the volume of the pyramid.

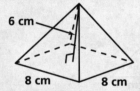

Find the surface area of each figure described. Round your answers to the nearest tenth.

15. a rectangular prism with a 5 in.-by-4 in. base and height 8 in.

16. a pyramid with a square base with sides 6 cm and slant height 12 cm

17. a sphere with radius 4 ft

Find each measure in ⊙*P*.

18. $m\widehat{LM}$

19. $m\widehat{LQN}$

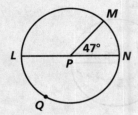

20. Find the area of a regular decagon with side length 5 in. and apothem 7.7 in.

21. Find the area of the shaded region to the nearest hundredth.

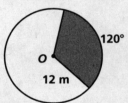

22 Find the area of a label on a soup can that has a height of 10 cm and a diameter of 6 cm. Round your answer to the nearest tenth.

Name _____ Class _____ Date _____

Quarter 4 Test

Form E

Chapters 10–12

1. Find the volume of the sphere to the nearest tenth.

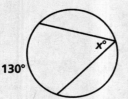

2. Two similar pentagons have corresponding sides in the ratio 3 : 8. Give the ratio of the perimeters and the ratio of the areas.

Find the value of *x*.

3.

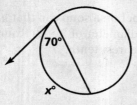

4.

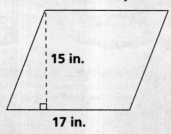

5. What is the measure of an interior angle of a regular hexagon?

  A. 135   **B.** 120

  C. 60   **D.** 45

6. Find the area of the parallelogram.

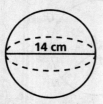

7. Find the value of *x*.

8. Find the surface area of the cylinder. Round your answer to the nearest tenth.

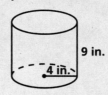

9. Find the area of the trapezoid.

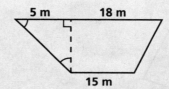

Use the figure for Exercises 10 and 11.

10. How many vertices does the figure have?

11. How many edges does the figure have?

Quarter 4 Test (continued) **Form E**

Chapters 10–12

Find m$\overparen{AB}$.

12.

13.
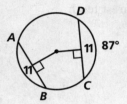

14. Find the volume of the pyramid.

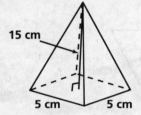

**Find the surface area of each figure described.
Round your answers to the nearest tenth.**

15. a sphere with diameter 16 m

16. a cone with radius 7 in. and slant height 15 in.

17. a rectangular prism with a 3-ft by 7-ft base and
height 11 ft

Find each measure in ⊙P.

18. m$\overparen{LM}$

19. m$\overparen{LQN}$

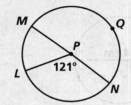

20. Find the area of a regular octagon with side
length 6 in. and apothem 7.24 in. Round your
answer to the nearest tenth.

21. Find the area of the shaded region to the
nearest hundredth.

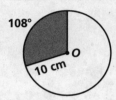

22. Find the area of a label on a soup can that has a
height of 5 in. and a diameter of 3.5 in. Round
your answer to the nearest tenth.

Mid-Course Test

Form D

Chapters 1–6

1. Find the next two terms in the sequence.

$1, -1, -3, -5, -7, \ldots$

2. Find the value of x if $DT = 100$.

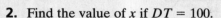

$D \qquad S \qquad T$
$(6x - 7) \quad (4x - 3)$

3. Find the value of x.

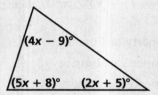

$(4x - 9)°$

$(5x + 8)° \qquad (2x + 5)°$

4. In $\triangle RST$, $RS = 18$, $ST = 24$, and $RT = 30$.
List the angles from smallest to largest.

5. Given $a \parallel b$ cut by transversal c, which of the
following statements is *not* true?

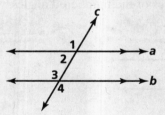

c

1
2
3
4

a
b

A. $\angle 1$ and $\angle 3$ are corresponding angles.

B. $\angle 2$ and $\angle 3$ are same-side interior angles.

C. $\angle 3$ and $\angle 4$ are vertical angles.

D. $\angle 1$ and $\angle 4$ are alternate interior angles.

6. Find the value of x.

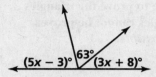

$(5x - 3)° \quad 63° \quad (3x + 8)°$

7. Which pair of lines is parallel?

F. $y = 5x + 3$
$\quad 5x + y = 10$

G. $y = -2x - 1$
$\quad 2x + y = 4$

H. $y = 3x + 8$
$\quad 3x + y = 6$

J. $x = 3$
$\quad y = 3$

8. What is the measure of an exterior angle of a
regular octagon?

9. A circle has radius 16 in. Find its circumference
and area to the nearest tenth.

10. What is the distance between $(-1, 6)$ and
$(5, -2)$?

11. Given rectangle $DJRT$, find the measures of
$\angle 1$ and $\angle 2$.

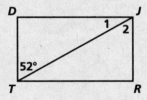

$D \qquad\qquad\qquad J$

1
2

$52°$

$T \qquad\qquad\qquad R$

Mid-Course Test (continued)

Form D

Chapters 1–6

For each pair of triangles, state the postulate or theorem you can use to prove the triangles congruent. If the triangles cannot be proven congruent, write *not possible*.

12.

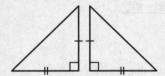

13.

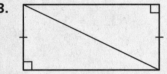

14.

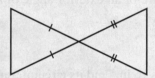

15.

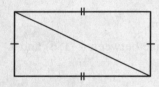

16.

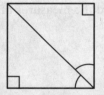

17.

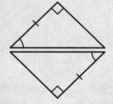

18. Find the length of $\overline{WZ}$.

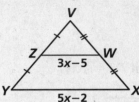

19. Which property is represented by the following statement?

If $m\angle ABC = 90$ *and* $m\angle XYZ = 90$, *then* $m\angle ABC = m\angle XYZ$.

A. Transitive Property of Equality

B. Symmetric Property of Equality

C. Reflexive Property of Equality

D. Addition Property of Equality

20. What is the slope of the line that contains $(6, -4)$ and $(-4, 1)$?

F. $\frac{1}{2}$ **G.** $-\frac{1}{2}$

H. 2 **J.** -2

21. Find the measures of the numbered angles.

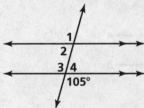

22. Name all the quadrilaterals whose diagonals bisect each other.

Mid-Course Test (continued)

Form D

Chapters 1–6

23. What is the most precise name for a quadrilateral with both pairs of opposite sides parallel and four right angles?

    A. parallelogram   **B.** rectangle

    C. rhombus   **D.** square

24. Identify the hypothesis and conclusion of the conditional.

If a transversal intersects two parallel lines, then alternate interior angles are congruent.

25. Which of the following is the converse of the conditional in Exercise 24?

    F. If two lines and a transversal form alternate interior angles that are supplementary, then the lines are perpendicular.

    G. Alternate interior angles formed by parallel lines are congruent.

    H. If a transversal intersects two parallel lines, then alternate interior angles are congruent.

    J. If two lines and a transversal form alternate interior angles that are congruent, then the lines are parallel.

26. If $\triangle DLQ \cong \triangle EMR$, then which of the following is *not* true?

    A. $\angle LDQ \cong \angle MRE$

    B. $\angle DLQ \cong \angle EMR$

    C. $\angle RME \cong \angle QLD$

    D. $\angle MRE \cong \angle LQD$

27. Find the perimeter of the polygon.

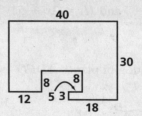

28. Graph a line parallel to $y = -2x - 2$ that contains $(-1, 2)$.

29. Graph a line perpendicular to $y = -\frac{1}{3}x + 2$ that contains $(1, 1)$.

30. Given rectangle *BCRS*, find the perimeter of $\triangle CRW$.

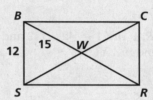

31. Find the coordinates of the midpoint of $(7, -2)$ and $(-5, 6)$.

32. The length of one side of a regular decagon is 12 cm. What is the perimeter of the decagon?

33. Find the measure of the sides of equilateral △JKL if $JK = 5x - 7$ and $JL = 2x + 5$.

34. What is the intersection of planes ADFE and EFCB?

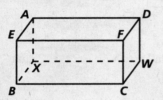

    F. plane DWCF

    G. $\overleftrightarrow{EF}$

    H. plane AXWD

    J. $\overleftrightarrow{BC}$

35. $\overrightarrow{QX}$ bisects ∠PQR. If $m\angle 1 = 4x - 12$ and $m\angle 2 = 2x + 6$, find $m\angle XQR$.

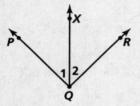

36. Find the value of x.

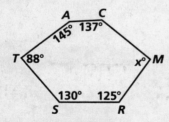

37. Find $m\angle BXC$.

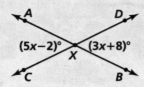

38. Which two sides must be congruent to use ASA to prove △DMX ≅ △JCX?

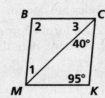

39. In parallelogram BCKM, find $m\angle 1, m\angle 2$, and $m\angle 3$.

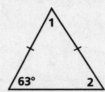

40. Find $m\angle 1$ and $m\angle 2$.

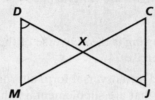

Mid-Course Test

Form E

Chapters 1–6

1. Find the next two terms in the sequence.

$1, -3, -7, -11, -15, \ldots$

2. Find the value of x if $PR = 120$.

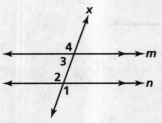

3. Find the value of x.

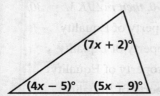

4. In $\triangle RST$, $m\angle R = 43$, $m\angle S = 71$, and $m\angle T = 66$. List the sides from largest to smallest.

5. Given $m \parallel n$ cut by transversal x, which of the following statements is *not* true?

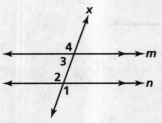

A. $\angle 2$ and $\angle 3$ are same-side interior angles.

B. $\angle 1$ and $\angle 3$ are alternate interior angles.

C. $\angle 1$ and $\angle 2$ are vertical angles.

D. $\angle 2$ and $\angle 4$ are corresponding angles.

6. Find the value of x.

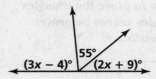

7. Which pair of lines is parallel?

F. $y = -3x + 1$
$3x + y = 8$

G. $y = 2x - 7$
$2x + y = -6$

H. $y = 4x + 3$
$4x + y = -6$

J. $x = -2$
$y = -2$

8. What is the measure of an exterior angle of a regular hexagon?

9. A circle has radius 15 in. Find its circumference and area to the nearest tenth.

10. What is the distance between $(8, 7)$ and $(3, -5)$?

11. Given rectangle $MNPT$, find $m\angle 1$ and $m\angle 2$.

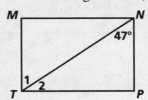

Mid-Course Test (continued) Form E

Chapters 1–6

For each pair of triangles, state the postulate or theorem you can use to prove the triangles congruent. If the triangles cannot be proven congruent, write *not possible*.

12.

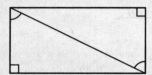

13.

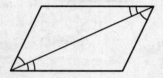

14.

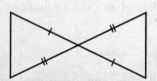

15.

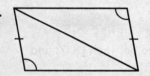

16.

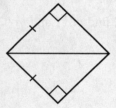

17.

18. Find the length of $\overline{BC}$.

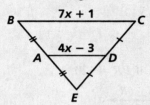

19. Which property is represented by the following statement?

If $3m\angle JKM = 90$, then $m\angle JKM = 30$.

A. Addition Property of Equality

B. Reflexive Property of Equality

C. Symmetric Property of Equality

D. Division Property of Equality

20. What is the slope of the line that contains $(4, -6)$ and $(-1, 4)$?

F. $\frac{1}{2}$ **G.** $-\frac{1}{2}$

H. 2 **J.** -2

21. Find the measures of the numbered angles.

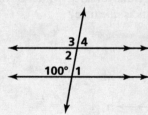

22. Name all the quadrilaterals that have diagonals that bisect opposite angles.

Mid-Course Test (continued)   Form E

Chapters 1–6

23. What is the most precise name for a quadrilateral with both pairs of opposite sides parallel?

   A. parallelogram   **B.** rectangle

   C. rhombus   **D.** square

24. Identify the hypothesis and conclusion of the conditional.

If a transversal intersects two parallel lines, then corresponding angles are congruent.

25. Which of the following is the converse of the conditional in Exercise 24?

   F. If two lines and a transversal form corresponding angles that are supplementary, then the lines are perpendicular.

   G. If a transversal intersects two parallel lines, then corresponding angles are congruent.

   H. If two lines and a transversal form corresponding angles that are congruent, then the lines are parallel.

   J. Corresponding angles formed by parallel lines are congruent.

26. If $\triangle BRX \cong \triangle EMS$, then which of the following is *not* true?

   A. $\angle EMS \cong \angle BRX$

   B. $\angle RBX \cong \angle MSE$

   C. $\angle SME \cong \angle XRB$

   D. $\angle MSE \cong \angle RXB$

27. Find the perimeter of the polygon.

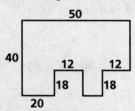

28. Graph a line parallel to $y = 3x - 1$ that contains $(2, 3)$.

29. Graph a line perpendicular to $y = \frac{1}{2}x - 5$ that contains $(-2, 2)$.

30. Given rectangle *CHKP*, find the perimeter of $\triangle PCX$.

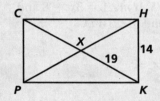

31. Find the coordinates of the midpoint of $(8, -5)$ and $(-4, 7)$.

32. The length of one side of a regular decagon is 16 cm. What is the perimeter of the decagon?

Mid-Course Test (continued)

Form E

Chapters 1–6

33. Find the measure of the sides of equilateral $\triangle DST$ if $DS = 6x - 7$ and $DT = 3x + 8$.

34. What is the intersection of planes $AXYC$ and $BWYC$?

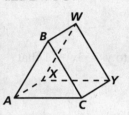

F. $\overleftrightarrow{AX}$

G. plane ABC

H. $\triangle ABC$

J. $\overleftrightarrow{CY}$

35. $\overrightarrow{DW}$ bisects $\angle BWS$. If $m\angle 1 = 3x + 8$ and $m\angle 2 = 4x - 5$, find $m\angle BWD$.

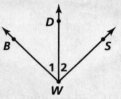

36. Find the value of x.

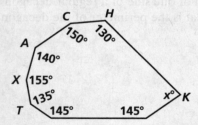

37. Find $m\angle MWT$.

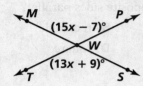

38. Which two sides must be shown congruent to use AAS to prove $\triangle MZW \cong \triangle TRW$?

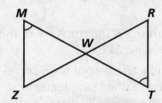

39. In parallelogram $CMWX$, find $m\angle 1, m\angle 2$, and $m\angle 3$.

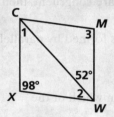

40. Find $m\angle 1$ and $m\angle 2$.

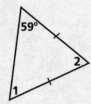

Final Test

Form D

Chapters 1–12

1. Find the values of *x* and *y*.

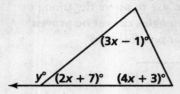

2. If △ADR is similar to a triangle whose sides have lengths 3, 7, and 6, which of the following could be the perimeter of △ADR?

A. 16 **B.** 32

C. 64 **D.** any of these

3. Identify the hypothesis and conclusion of the conditional.

If two sides of a triangle are congruent, then the angles opposite those sides are also congruent.

4. Which of the following is the converse of the conditional in Exercise 3?

F. If two angles of a triangle are congruent, then the triangles are congruent by the AAA Postulate.

G. If two angles of a triangle are congruent, then the triangles are congruent.

H. If two angles of a triangle are congruent, then the sides opposite the angles are also congruent.

J. If two angles of a triangle are not congruent, then the sides opposite the angles are congruent.

5. What is the equation of a line parallel to $y = \frac{1}{2}x - 1$ that contains $(6, -4)$?

A. $x - 2y = 14$ **B.** $x - 2y = -20$

C. $x - 2y = -1$ **D.** $x - 2y = 8$

6. Find the length of $\overline{RS}$.

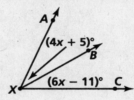

7. $\overrightarrow{XB}$ bisects ∠AXC. Find m∠AXC.

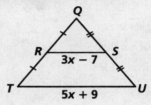

8. Given △ABC ~ △DEF with a scale factor of 5 : 7. If △ABC has perimeter 65, what is the perimeter of △DEF?

9. If △HLM ≅ △RST, then which of the following is *not* necessarily true?

F. ∠SRT ≅ ∠LHM **G.** ∠RTS ≅ ∠MLH

H. ∠STR ≅ ∠LMH **J.** ∠TRS ≅ ∠MHL

Final Test (continued)

Form D

Chapters 1–12

Use the figure below for Exercises 10–13.

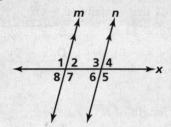

Identify the pairs of angles as:

    A. alternate interior angles

    B. same-side interior angles

    C. corresponding angles

    D. vertical angles

10. ∠2 and ∠3

11. ∠6 and ∠8

12. ∠3 and ∠7

13. ∠1 and ∠7

14. A circle has radius 11 in. Find its area and circumference to the nearest tenth.

15. Find the coordinates of the midpoint of $(-8, -3)$ and $(2, -5)$.

16. Write the equation of a line in slope-intercept form that is perpendicular to $y = x + 4$ and contains $(3, -2)$.

For each pair of triangles, state the postulate or theorem you can use to prove the triangles congruent. If the triangles cannot be proven congruent, write *not possible.*

17.

18.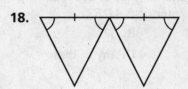

19.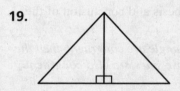

20.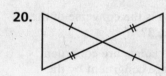

21.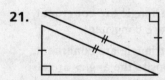

Final Test (continued)

Form D

Chapters 1–12

22. Find the values of x and y. Leave your answers in simplest radical form.

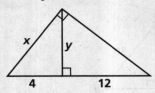

23. The lengths of the sides of a right triangle are 15 m, 20 m, and 25 m. What is the area of the triangle?

F. 150 m²
G. 187.5 m²
H. 300 m²
J. 750 m²

24. Find the volume of the cylinder in terms of π.

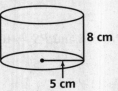

25. Find the value of x.

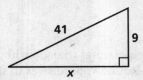

26. Determine which of the following will *not* tessellate.

A. hexagon
B. octagon
C. rectangle
D. triangle

27. Determine the angle of rotation of Figure 1 to Figure 2.

Figure 1   Figure 2

28. Given $ABCD \sim WXYZ$. If the area of $ABCD$ is 25 m², what is the area of $WXYZ$?

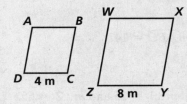

29. Find the height of a regular square prism with a base edge of 4 ft and volume of 176 ft³.

30. What is the distance between $(6, -7)$ and $(-2, 8)$?

31. Find the value of x. Assume that segments that appear to be tangent are tangent.

F. 180
G. 120
H. 60
J. 50

Final Test (continued)   Form D

Chapters 1–12

Use the figure below for Exercises 32–34.

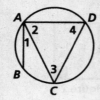

32. Find $m\angle 1$ if $m\overset{\frown}{BC} = 56$.

33. Find $m\angle 4$ if $m\overset{\frown}{ABC} = 142$.

34. Find $m\overset{\frown}{BCD}$ if $m\angle 1 = 25$ and $m\angle 2 = 65$.

35. Classify the triangle as right, acute, or obtuse if the measures of its sides are 28, 46, and 53.

36. Find the center and radius of the circle with equation $(x + 4)^2 + (x - 3)^2 = 49$.

37. Find the lengths of AC and CD. Round your answers to the nearest tenth.

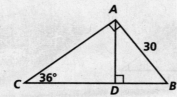

38. Find the area of the trapezoid.

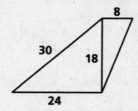

39. Find the value of x if $PR = 6$ and $PS = 10$.

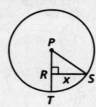

40. Find the area of an equilateral triangle with perimeter of 30 cm. Round your answer to the nearest hundredth.

Final Test

Form E

Chapters 1–12

1. Find the values of *x* and *y*.

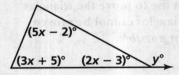

2. If △*DHT* is similar to a triangle whose sides have lengths 4, 7, and 9, which of the following could be the perimeter of △*DHT*?

A. 20   **B.** 40

C. 60   **D.** any of these

3. Identify the hypothesis and conclusion of the conditional.

If a point is on the perpendicular bisector of a segment, then it is equidistant from the endpoints of the segment.

4. Which of the following is the converse of the conditional in Exercise 3?

F. If a point is congruent from the endpoints of a segment, then it is on the perpendicular bisector of the segment.

G. If a point is equidistant from a segment, then it is on a segment perpendicular to the bisector.

H. If a point is not on the perpendicular bisector of a segment, then it is not equidistant from the endpoints of the segment.

J. If a point is equidistant from the endpoints of a segment, then it is on the perpendicular bisector of the segment.

5. What is the equation of a line perpendicular to $y = -\frac{1}{2}x - 1$ that contains $(4, -3)$?

A. $2x - y = 11$ **B.** $x - 2y = 10$

C. $2x - y = 5$ **D.** $x - 2y = -2$

6. Find the length of *BD*.

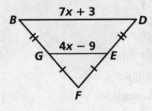

7. $\overrightarrow{YW}$ bisects ∠*XYZ*. Find *m*∠*XYZ*.

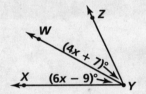

8. Given △*JKL* ~ △*MNP* with a scale factor of 3 : 4. If △*JKL* has perimeter 57, what is the perimeter of △*MNP*?

9. If △*KLM* ≅ △*BCS*, then which of the following is *not* true?

F. ∠*CBS* ≅ ∠*LKM*   **G.** ∠*MKL* ≅ ∠*SCB*

H. ∠*BSC* ≅ ∠*KML*   **J.** ∠*LMK* ≅ ∠*CSB*

Final Test (continued)

Form E

Chapters 1–12

Use the figure below for Exercises 10–13.

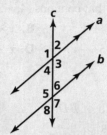

Identify the pairs of angles as:

    A. alternate interior angles

    B. corresponding angles

    C. same-side interior angles

    D. vertical angles

10. $\angle 4$ and $\angle 6$

11. $\angle 5$ and $\angle 7$

12. $\angle 3$ and $\angle 6$

13. $\angle 1$ and $\angle 5$

14. A circle has radius 17 m. Find its area and circumference to the nearest tenth.

15. Find the coordinates of the midpoint of $(9, 1)$ and $(3, -5)$.

16. Write the equation of a line in slope-intercept form that is parallel to $y = -x + 8$ and contains $(-3, -5)$.

For each pair of triangles, state the postulate or theorem you can use to prove the triangles congruent. If the triangles cannot be proven congruent, write *not possible*.

17.

18.

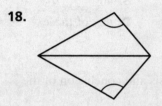

19.

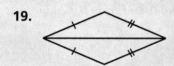

20.

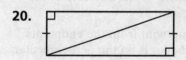

21.

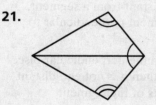

Final Test (continued)   Form E

Chapters 1–12

22. Find the values of *x* and *y*. Leave your answers in simplest radical form.

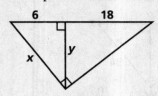

27. Determine the angle of rotation of Figure 1 to Figure 2.

Figure 1   Figure 2

23. The lengths of the sides of a right triangle are 18 ft, 24 ft, and 30 ft. What is the area of the triangle?

F. 216 ft^2 **G.** 270 ft^2

H. 432 ft^2 **J.** cannot be determined

28. Given *CKMS* ~ *DLNT*. If the area of *CKMS* is 32 cm^2, what is the area of *DLNT*?

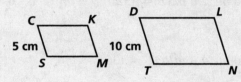

24. Find the volume of the cylinder in terms of π.

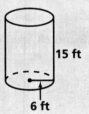

15 ft

6 ft

29. Find the height of a regular square prism with a base edge of 6 ft and volume of 504 ft^3.

30. What is the distance between $(-12, 6)$ and $(8, -9)$?

25. Find the value of *x*.

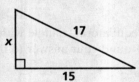

17

x

15

31. Find the value of *x*. Assume that segments that appear to be tangent are tangent.

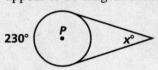

230°   *P*   *x*°

F. 40   **G.** 50

H. 60   **J.** 100

26. Determine which of the following will tessellate.

A. decagon   **B.** pentagon

C. octagon   **D.** triangle

Final Test (continued)

Form E

Chapters 1–12

Use the figure below for Exercises 32–34.

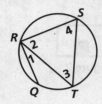

32. Find $m\angle 2$ if $m\widehat{ST} = 132$.

33. Find $m\angle 4$ if $m\widehat{RQT} = 136$.

34. Find $m\widehat{QTS}$ if $m\angle 1 = 27$ and $m\angle 2 = 60$.

35. Classify the triangle as right, acute, or obtuse if the measures of its sides are 31, 45, and 56.

36. Find the center and radius of the circle with equation $(x + 6)^2 + (x - 5)^2 = 64$.

37. Find the lengths of $\overline{MW}$ and $\overline{MX}$. Round your answers to the nearest tenth.

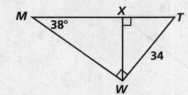

38. Find the area of the trapezoid.

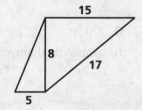

39. Find the value of x if $BD = 8$ and $BC = 17$.

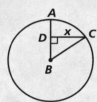

40. Find the area of an equilateral triangle with perimeter of 60 in. Round your answer to the nearest hundredth.

Answers

Chapter 1 Test, Form F

1. Multiply by 3; 81, 243. **2.** Add 11, add 9, add 11, add 9, and so on; 44, 55. **3.** Insert one more dot; a circle with three dots, a circle with four dots

4. The relationship $\frac{(x-1)+(x+1)}{2} = x$ is true for all whole numbers x. No counterexample exists.

5. Sample:

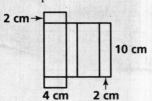

2 cm, 10 cm, 4 cm, 2 cm

6. Sample:

8 in., 22 in.

7. M, E, B, and D **8.** C, M, and O or M, B, and E
9. Sample: A, F, O, and D **10a.** M **10b.** M
10c. F **10d.** O **11.** $\angle AOB$ **12.** $\angle DOE$
13. $\angle COD$ **14.** $\angle AOE$ and $\angle BOC$ or $\angle AOB$ and $\angle COE$ **15a.** 5 **15b.** 9 **15c.** 48 **16.** 25
17. 25 **18.** 130 **19.** 180 **20.** 140°; obtuse
21. 63°; acute

22.

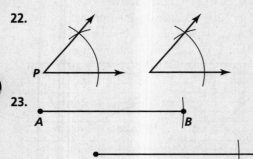

23.

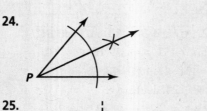

A, B

24.

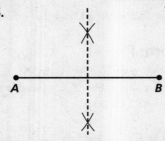

P

25.

A, B

26. 5 **27.** 17.3 **28.** (9, 18) **29.** 58 in.; 168 in.^{2}
30. 38 cm; 78 cm^2 **31.** 8π in.; 16π in.^{2}
32. 30π cm; 225π cm^2

Chapter 1 Test, Form G

1. multiply by 2; 48, 96 **2.** add 4; 24, 28 **3.** Add another row of dots with one more dot than the previous row, a figure with 10 dots

5. The relationship $\frac{(x-2)+(x+2)}{2} = x$ is true for all whole numbers x. No counterexample exists.

5. Sample:

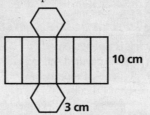

10 cm, 3 cm

6. Sample:

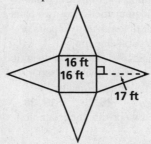

16 ft, 16 ft, 17 ft

7. Sample: A, B, E **8.** Sample: F, C, G
9. Sample: A, B, D, H **10a.** C **10b.** C
11. $\angle LPJ$ **12.** $\angle LPK$ **13.** $\angle NPO$
14. $\angle LPK$ and $\angle NPO$ or $\angle MPN$ and $\angle JPK$
15a. 3 **15b.** 13 **15c.** 5
16. 82 **17.** 98 **18.** 41 **19.** 82
20. 90; right **21.** 150; obtuse
22.

A, B

23.

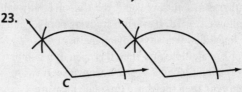

C

24.

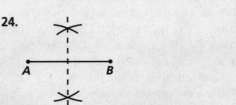

A, B

Answers (continued)

25.

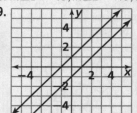

26. 9 **27.** 8.1 **28.** $(3, 3)$ **29.** 36 ft; 81 ft^2
30. 44 in.; 85 in.^{2} **31.** 10π cm; 25π cm^2
32. 14π in.; 49π in.^{2}

Chapter 2 Test, Form F
1a. If a polygon has five sides, then it is a pentagon.
1b. true **2a.** If Mary lives in Minnesota, then she lives in
Minneapolis. **2b.** false **3.** Reflexive Property of
Equality **4.** Substitution Property of Equality
5. Division Property of Equality **6.** Distributive Property
7a. 38 **7b.** 128 **7c.** 26 **7d.** 154 **8.** 50
9. 13.5 **10.** 4 **11.** Martina is quick. **12.** If I
don't wear sunscreen while swimming, then I'll be in pain.
13. If a quadrilateral is a parallelogram, then it has two pairs
of opposite sides parallel. If a quadrilateral has two pairs of
opposite sides parallel, then it is a parallelogram.
14. A rectangle has four right angles. **15.** good definition
16. An octopus has eight legs. **17a.** Division Property of
Equality **17b.** Subtraction Property of Equality
17c. Division Property of Equality **18.** 17 **19.** 28
20. Answers may vary. There are two possibilities. Samples:
$(4, -2)$ or $(-2, 5)$

Chapter 2 Test, Form G
1. Hypothesis: a triangle has three congruent sides; conclusion:
the triangle is equilateral. **2.** Hypothesis: Tyler lives in
San Francisco; conclusion: Tyler lives in California.
3. Relexive Property **4.** Transitive Property
5. Division Property of Equality **6.** Subtraction Property
of Equality **7a.** 75 **7b.** 90 **7c.** 15 **7d.** 105
8. 6 **9.** 22 **15** Juan is on the soccer team.
16. Figure $WXYZ$ has two pairs of parallel sides.
17. If the weather is nice this weekend, the Carson family will
roast marshmallows. **18.** If you are studying parallel and
perpendicular lines, then you are studying math.
19. If a number is a multiple of 2, then it is even. If a number
is even, then it is a multiple of 2. **20.** Converse: If two
angles are congruent, then they have the same measure.
Biconditional: Two angles have the same measure if and only
if they are congruent. **21.** Converse: If a quadrilateral has
four congruent sides, then it is a square. **22.** Converse: If
$|x| = 5$, then $x = 5$. **23.** Converse: If you live in the
capital of Massachusetts, then you live in Boston.
Biconditional: You live in Boston if and only if you live in the
capital of Massachusetts. **24a.** Subtraction Property of
Equality **24b.** Multiplication Property of Equality
25. 35 **26.** 14 **27.** 68

Chapter 3 Test, Form F
1. true **2.** true **3.** false **4.** true **5.** false
6. $m\angle 1 = 62, m\angle 2 = 62$, alternate interior angles
7. $m\angle 1 = 85, m\angle 2 = 95$, same-side interior angles
8. $m\angle 1 = 75, m\angle 2 = 75$, alternate interior angles
9. 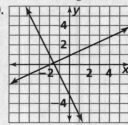 **10.**

11. $\overline{AD}$ and $\overline{WZ}$ **12.** $\overline{AD}$ and $\overline{WZ}$ **13.** $\overline{AD}$ and $\overline{WZ}$
14. $\overline{AW}$ and $\overline{DZ}$ **15.** $x = 92, y = 88$ **16.** $w = 31$,
$x = 65, y = 65, z = 115$ **17.** 1440 **18.** 45
19. neither **20.** perpendicular **21.** parallel
22. $y = 3x - 1$ **23.** $y = \frac{1}{4}x - 3$ **24.** $y = -2x - 2$

Chapter 3 Test, Form G
1. true **2.** false **3.** true **4.** false **5.** true
6. $m\angle 1 = 65, m\angle 2 = 65$, alternate interior angles
7. $m\angle 1 = 84, m\angle 2 = 96$, same-side interior angles
8. $m\angle 1 = 70, m\angle 2 = 70$, alternate interior angles
9. 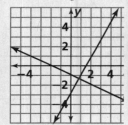 **10.**

11. $\overline{AD}$ and $\overline{BC}$ **12.** $\overline{AD}$ and $\overline{BC}$ **13.** $\overline{AD}$ and $\overline{BC}$
14. $\overline{AB}$ and $\overline{DC}$ **15.** $x = 97, y = 83$ **16.** $x = 60$,
$y = 60, z = 120, w = 34$ **17.** 1080 **18.** 36
19. parallel **20.** neither **21.** neither
22. $y = -3x + 7$ **23.** $y = -2x - 4$ **24.** $y = 2x + 3$

Chapter 4 Test, Form F
1. $x = 58, y = 64$ **2.** $a = 40, b = 70, c = 70$ **3.** SSS
4. SAS **5.** HL **6.** AAS **7.** not possible **8.** not possible
9. SSS or SAS **10.** SSS or SAS **11.** ASA
12.

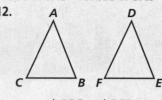

$\triangle ABC \cong \triangle DEF$

$\angle A \cong \angle D; \angle B \cong \angle E; \angle C \cong \angle F; \overline{AB} \cong \overline{DE};$
$\overline{AC} \cong \overline{DF}; \overline{BC} \cong \overline{EF}$ **13.** B **14.** $\overline{AB} \cong \overline{XY};$

Informal Geometry Lesson Plans and Assessments

Answers (continued)

$\overline{BC} \cong \overline{YZ}$; $\overline{AC} \cong \overline{XZ}$ **15.** $\angle A \cong \angle X$; $\angle B \cong \angle Y$; $\angle C \cong \angle Z$ **16.** C **17.** J

Chapter 4 Test, Form G

1. $a = 63, b = 63, c = 54$ **2.** $x = 59, y = 59$ **3.** SAS
4. not possible **5.** SSS **6.** HL **7.** SAS **8.** HL
9. SAS or ASA **10.** SSS **11.** AAS

12.

$\triangle DEF \cong \triangle RST$

$\angle D \cong \angle R$; $\angle E \cong \angle S$; $\angle F \cong \angle T$; $\overline{DE} \cong \overline{RS}$;
$\overline{EF} \cong \overline{ST}$; $\overline{DF} \cong \overline{RT}$ **13.** C **14.** $\angle J \cong \angle P$;
$\angle K \cong \angle Q$; $\angle L \cong \angle R$ **15.** $\overline{JK} \cong \overline{PQ}$; $\overline{KL} \cong \overline{QR}$;
$\overline{JL} \cong \overline{PR}$ **16.** A **17.** B

Chapter 5 Test, Form F

1. 4 **2.** 4.5 **3.** 6.5 **4.** 5 **5.** Sample: $VP = RT$ **6.** $\angle D$,
$\angle B, \angle C$ **7.** $\angle C, \angle D, \angle B$ **8.** C **9.** 3; 21 **10.** inside
11. inside **12.** on **13.** $\overline{BC}$ **14.** $\overline{LO}, \overline{LM}, \overline{MO}, \overline{MN}, \overline{NO}$
15. 3 **16.** 25 **17.** 6

Chapter 5 Test, Form G

1. 6 **2.** 4 **3.** 54 **4.** 3 **5.** Sample: $EK = GI$ **6.** $\angle B$,
$\angle C, \angle D$ **7.** $\angle D, \angle C, \angle B$ **8.** A **9.** 5; 17 **10.** centroid
11. orthocenter **12.** circumcenter **13.** $\overline{JK}$ **14.** $\overline{YZ}, \overline{XY}$,
$\overline{XZ}, \overline{WX}, \overline{WZ}$ **15.** 3 **16.** 30 **17.** 20

Chapter 6 Test, Form F

1.

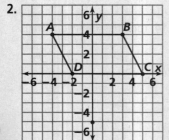

square

2.

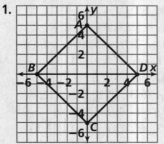

parallelogram

3.

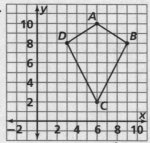

kite

4.

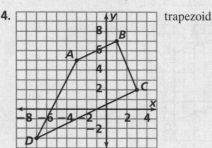

trapezoid

5. 7 in. **6.** 6 cm **7.** 22 m **8.** $x = 3.5$ **9.** $x = 19; y = 123$
10. $x = 6$ **11.** 78; 102 **12.** 90; 61 **13.** 64; 128 **14.** 90; 63;
27 **15.** 90; 45; 45 **16.** 71; 71; 38 **17.** parallelogram
18. rhombus **19.** trapezoid **20.** square

Chapter 6 Test, Form G

1.

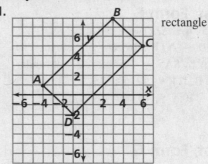

rectangle

2.

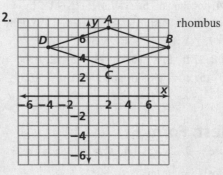

rhombus

Answers (continued)

3.

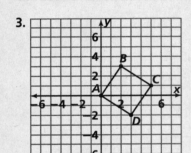

square

4.

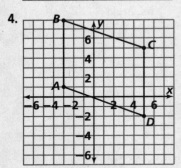

parallelogram

5. 7 ft **6.** 18 in. **7.** 2 m **8.** $x = 15$ **9.** $x = 17$
10. $x = 12; y = 49$ **11.** 90; 45; 45 **12.** 26; 77; 77 **13.** 116;
32; 64 **14.** 90; 71 **15.** 90; 34 **16.** 64; 116 **17.** square
18. kite **19.** rhombus **20.** trapezoid

Chapter 7 Test, Form F

1. 21 **2.** 3.5 **3.** 12.5 **4.** $\triangle SLQ \sim \triangle NTR$ by SSS $\sim$
Theorem **5.** $\triangle MBD \sim \triangle FWY$ by AA $\sim$ Postulate
6. $\triangle PRG \sim \triangle KRN$ by SAS $\sim$ Theorem **7.** not similar
8. 9.6 m **9.** 15 **10.** B **11.** 9 **12.** 6.4 **13.** 3 : 1 **14.** 2 : 3
15. $x = 27$ **16.** $x = 10; y = 4.5$ **17.** 4.8

Chapter 7 Test, Form G

1. 22 **2.** $\frac{9}{4}$ **3.** 9 **4.** not similar **5.** $\triangle KLM \sim \triangle QXA$ by
SAS $\sim$ Theorem or AA $\sim$ Postulate **6.** $\triangle DJH \sim \triangle SJP$ by
SAS $\sim$ Theorem **7.** $\triangle VWX \sim \triangle MON$ by
SSS $\sim$ Theorem **8.** 27 ft **9.** 8 **10.** C **11.** 7.2 **12.** 7.5
13. 1 : 4 **14.** 5 : 3 **15.** $x = \sqrt{89}$ or about 9.43; $y = 12.8$
16. 12 **17.** 2.4

Chapter 8 Test, Form F

1. right **2.** obtuse **3.** $2\sqrt{85}$ **4.** $x = 4\sqrt{3}; y = 8\sqrt{3}$
5. $\sin T = \frac{6\sqrt{2}}{19}; \cos T = \frac{17}{19}; \tan T = \frac{6\sqrt{2}}{17}$
6. $\sin T = \frac{14}{17}; \cos T = \frac{\sqrt{93}}{17}; \tan T = \frac{14\sqrt{93}}{93}$ **7.** 60
8. 15.3 **9.** 63 **10.** 36.9 **11.** 78.7 **12.** Angle 1 is
the angle of depression from the cloud to the person in the
castle. Angle 2 is the angle of elevation from the person in the
castle to the cloud. Angle 3 is the angle of depression from the
person in the castle to the person on the ground. Angle 4 is the

angle of elevation from the person on the ground to the castle
13. $\approx$ 1710 ft
14. $\sin x° = \frac{\text{opposite}}{\text{hypotenuse}}$ and $\cos x° = \frac{\text{adjacent}}{\text{hypotenuse}}$

$\frac{\sin x°}{\cos x°} = \frac{\text{opposite}}{\text{hypotenuse}} \div \frac{\text{adjacent}}{\text{hypotenuse}} =$

$\frac{\text{opposite}}{\text{hypotenuse}} \cdot \frac{\text{hypotenuse}}{\text{adjacent}} =$

$\frac{\text{opposite}}{\text{adjacent}} = \tan x°$

Chapter 8 Test, Form G

1. obtuse **2.** obtuse **3.** $x = 4\sqrt{15}$
4. $x = 6\sqrt{2}; y = 6\sqrt{2}$
5. $\sin A = \frac{\sqrt{15}}{8}; \cos A = \frac{7}{8}; \tan A = \frac{\sqrt{15}}{7}$
6. $\sin A = \frac{4}{5}; \cos A = \frac{3}{5}; \tan A = \frac{4}{3}$ **7.** 48 **8.** 8.6 **9.** 47
10. 33.7 **11.** 71.6 **12.** Angle 1 is the angle of elevation from
the person in the boat to the top of the lighthouse. Angle 2 is
the angle of depression from the top of the lighthouse to the
person in the boat. Angle 3 is the angle of elevation from the
top of the lighthouse to the cloud. Angle 4 is the angle of
depression from the cloud to the top of the lighthouse
13. 42 ft
14. $\sin x° = \frac{\text{opposite}}{\text{hypotenuse}}, \cos x° = \frac{\text{adjacent}}{\text{hypotenuse}},$

and $\tan x° = \frac{\text{opposite}}{\text{adjacent}}$

$\frac{\cos x°}{\sin x°} \cdot \tan x° = \frac{\text{adjacent}}{\text{hypotenuse}} \div \frac{\text{opposite}}{\text{hypotenuse}} \cdot \frac{\text{opposite}}{\text{adjacent}} =$

$\frac{\text{adjacent}}{\text{hypotenuse}} \cdot \frac{\text{hypotenuse}}{\text{opposite}} \cdot \frac{\text{opposite}}{\text{adjacent}} = 1$

Chapter 9 Test, Form F

1. Yes; the figures are the same shape and size. **2.** No;
the figures are not the same size. **3.** Yes; the figures are the
same shape and size. **4.** $(x, y) \rightarrow (x - 6, y + 1)$
5. $(x, y) \rightarrow (x + 3, y - 7)$ **6.** $A'(0, -3), B'(-4, 0),$
$C'(-6, -4), D'(-3, -5)$ **7.** $A'(6, 3), B'(10, 0), C'(12, 4),$
$D'(9, 5)$ **8.** $A'(3, 8), B'(-1, 5), C'(-3, 9), D'(0, 10)$
9. $A'(5, 2), B'(1, -1), C'(-1, 3), D'(2, 4)$ **10.** $A'(-3, 0),$
$B'(0, -4), C'(-4, -6), D'(-5, -3)$ **11.** $A'(0, 3), B'(4, 6),$
$C'(6, 2), D'(3, 1)$ **12.** $(x, y) \rightarrow (x + 4, y - 3)$
13. $(x, y) \rightarrow (x - 3, y + 6)$ **14.** rhombus and two triangles;
translation

Answers (continued)

15.

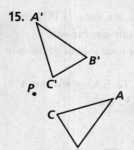

16.

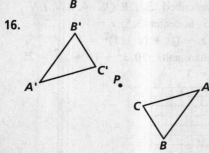

17. 180° rotational symmetry
18. line symmetry

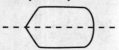

19. line symmetry; 180° rotational symmetry

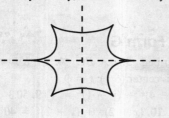

20. $(-7, 0)$ **21.** $(0, -3)$ **22.** $(-6, 1)$ **23.** $(-9, -4)$
24. $(2, -2)$ **25.** $(-5, 11)$

Chapter 9 Test, Form G

1. No; the figures are not the same shape.   **2.** Yes; the figures are the same shape and size.   **3.** Yes; the figures are the same shape and size.   **4.** $(-3, -4)$ **5.** $(10, 5)$ **6.** $A'(-3, 0)$, $B'(-5, -3)$, $C'(-2, -6)$, $D'(-1, -2)$ **7.** $A'(3, 4)$, $B'(5, 7)$, $C'(2, 10)$, $D'(1, 6)$ **8.** $A'(6, 4)$, $B'(8, 1)$, $C'(5, -2)$, $D'(4, 2)$
9. $A'(-2, 2)$, $B'(0, -1)$, $C'(-3, -4)$, $D'(-4, 0)$
10. $A'(-3, 0)$, $B'(-5, 3)$, $C'(-2, 6)$, $D'(-1, 2)$ **11.** $A'(3, 0)$, $B'(6, 2)$, $C'(9, -1)$, $D'(5, -2)$ **12.** $(x, y) \rightarrow (x - 6, y - 3)$
13. $(x, y) \rightarrow (x + 3, y + 2)$ **14.** hexagon and six triangles; translation

15.

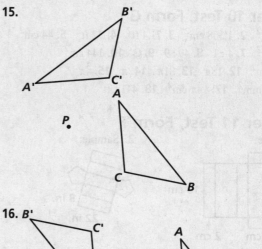

16.

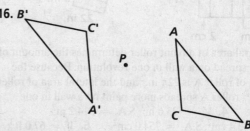

17. line symmetry

18. 90° rotational symmetry
19. line symmetry; 180° rotational symmetry

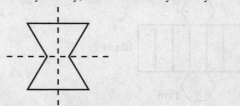

20. $(0, 3)$ **21.** $(5, 0)$ **22.** $(7, -2)$ **23.** $(-11, 8)$
24. $(4, -3)$ **25.** $(1, 6)$

Chapter 10 Test, Form F

1. 110.9 ft^2 **2.** 649.5 cm^2; 649.6 cm^2; or 649.7 cm^2
3. 40.2 ft^2 **4.** 60 ft^2 **5.** 92 cm^2 **6.** 72 in.^{2}
7. $\frac{16}{81}$ **8.** $\frac{1}{4}$ **9.** A   **10.** 360 in.^{2} **11.** 288 ft^2
12. 36π **13.** 324π **14.** 4π **15.** 18π
16. 75.4 cm^2 **17.** 144π cm^2 **18.** 4π in.^{2}

Answers (continued)

Chapter 10 Test, Form G

1. 292.7 ft^2 **2.** 1,368 cm^2 **3.** 71.4 ft^2 **4.** 72 ft^2 **5.** 44 cm^2
6. 66.3 in.^{2} **7.** 4 : 1 **8.** 49 : 9 **9.** C **10.** 144 cm^2
11. 375 cm^2 **12.** 18π **13.** 81π **14.** π **15.** $\frac{3}{2}\pi$
16. 18.27 mm^2 **17.** 14π cm^2 **18.** 441π ft^2

Chapter 11 Test, Form F

1. Sample:

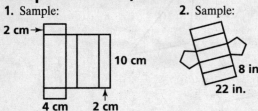

2. Sample:

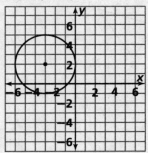

3. The lateral area of a paint roller determines the amount of paint it can spread on a wall in one revolution. Because the lateral area of roller A is 22π in.^{2} and the lateral area of roller B is 21π in.^{2}, roller A spreads more paint on a wall in one revolution. **4.** $V = 523.6$ m^3; S.A. $= 314.2$ m^2
5. $V = 1583.4$ cm^3; S.A. $= 754.0$ cm^2 **6.** $V = 67.0$ ft^3; S.A. $= 138.2$ ft^2 **7.** $V = 880.0$ in.^{3}; S.A. $= 696.0$ in.^{2}
8a. half of a sphere and a cone **8b.** 301.6 cm^2
9. Two regular cans of soup each have a volume of 461.8 cm^3 for a total of 923.6 cm^3. The single family-size can with its volume of 942.5 cm^3 is larger than the total volume of the two regular cans. **10.** D **11.** S.A. $= 1357.2$ m^2; $V = 4071.5$ m^3 **12.** S.A. $= 3296.8$ cm^2; $V = 12,113.3$ cm^3

Chapter 11 Test, Form G

1. Sample:

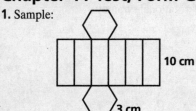

2. Sample:

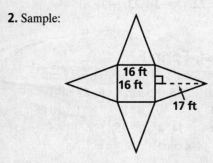

3. Roller A; the lateral area of roller A is 24π in.^{2}, and the lateral area of roller B is 18π in.^{2} **4.** $V = 408$ in.^{3}; S.A. $= 456$ in.^{2} **5.** $V = 523.6$ m^3; S.A. $= 314.2$ m^2 **6.** $V = 308$ cm^3; S.A. $= 298$ cm^2 **7.** $V = 1,017.9$ ft^3; S.A. $= 678.6$ in.^{2}
8a. cone and half of a sphere **8b.** 150.7 cm^2

9. Two regular cans of soup each have a volume of 141.3 cm^3 for a total of 282.6 cm^3. The single family-size can with its volume of 301.4 cm^3 is larger than the total volume of the two regular cans. **10.** D
11. S.A. $= 427.3$ m^2; $V = 611.4$ m^3 **12.** S.A. $= 864$ cm^2; $V = 1,824$ cm^3 3296.8 cm^2; $V = 12,113.3$ cm^3

Chapter 12 Test, Form F

1. inscribed **2.** circumscribed **3.** $\angle R; \widehat{QS}$ **4.** $\angle M; \widehat{LN}$
5. center $(0, 0); r = 5$ **6.** center $(3, 5); r = 10$
7. $x^2 + y^2 = 9$ **8.** $(x - 4)^2 + (y + 1)^2 = 4$
9. 37.7 units; 113.1 square units **10.** $x^2 + (y + 1)^2 = 25$
11. center $(-3, 2); r = 3$

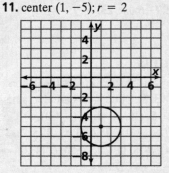

12. 90 **13.** 106 **14.** 105 **15.** 90 **16.** 45 **17.** 90 **18.** 180
19. 270

Chapter 12 Test, Form G

1. circumscribed **2.** inscribed **3.** $\angle A; \widehat{BC}$ **4.** $\angle J; \widehat{KI}$
5. center $(0, 0); r = 4$ **6.** center $(6, 1); r = 9$
7. $x^2 + y^2 = 25$ **8.** $(x + 4)^2 + (y - 1)^2 = 4$ **9.** 50.3 units; 201.1 square units **10.** $(x + 2)^2 + (y - 2)^2 = 40$
11. center $(1, -5); r = 2$

12. 90 **13.** 90 **14.** 120 **15.** 100 **16.** 65 **17.** 65 **18.** 130
19. 230

Informal Geometry Lesson Plans and Assessments

Answers (continued)

Quarter 1 Test, Form D

1. 21, 25 **2.** scalene triangle **3.** 36π m^2 **4.** A **5.** 5 **6.** 9
7.

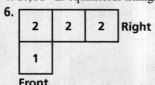

3	1	Right
2		

Front

8. 138 **9.** 46 **10.** C **11.** 40 cm **12.** $\overline{BF}$ **13.** 10π m
14. 120 **15.** $(-2, 4)$ **16.** $\frac{1}{2}$ **17.** B **18.** 5 **19.** 45 **20.** 90
21. 60 **22.** 85 **23.** hypothesis: two angles have a sum of 180°; conclusion: the angles are supplementary angles
24. G **25.** D

Quarter 1 Test, Form E

1. 26, 31 **2.** equilateral triangle **3.** 100π m^2 **4.** 5 **5.** 6
6.

2	2	2	Right
1			

Front

7. 110 **8.** 70 **9.** B **10.** G **11.** 60 in. **12.** $\overleftrightarrow{AB}$ **13.** 14π m
14. 135 **15.** $(1, 5)$ **16.** $-\frac{1}{3}$ **17.** D **18.** 10 **19.** 72 **20.** 55
21. 50 **22.** 75 **23.** G **24.** Hypothesis: two lines form right angles; conclusion: the lines are perpendicular. **25.** C

Quarter 2 Test, Form D

1. $\overline{XZ}$ **2.** 4 **3.** D **4.** 55 **5.** $x = 85, y = 60$ **6.** J
7. $\angle C, \angle A, \angle B$ **8.** $m\angle 1 = 54.5, m\angle 2 = 54.5, m\angle 3 = 71$
9. D **10.** C **11.** B **12.** E **13.** 55 **14.** 56 **15.** H
16. $m\angle 1 = 55, m\angle 2 = 45, m\angle 3 = 45$, **17.** $m\angle 1 = 25,$
$m\angle 2 = 25, m\angle 3 = 130$ **18.** A **19.** parallelogram, rectangle, square, rhombus **20.** 164 **21.** $\angle B \cong \angle D$
22. altitude **23.** 33

Quarter 2 Test, Form E

1. $\angle R$ **2.** 5 **3.** C **4.** 50, 65 **5.** $x = 100, y = 80$ **6.** F
7. $\angle C, \angle B, \angle A$ **8.** $m\angle 1 = 122, m\angle 2 = 29, m\angle 3 = 29$
9. E **10.** A **11.** C **12.** B **13.** 78 **14.** 58 **15.** G
16. $m\angle 1 = 44, m\angle 2 = 84, m\angle 3 = 40$ **17.** $m\angle 1 = 65,$
$m\angle 2 = 65, m\angle 3 = 50$ **18.** D **19.** parallelogram, rectangle, square, rhombus **20.** 187 **21.** $\overline{BX} \cong \overline{DX}$
22. perpendicular bisector **23.** 40

Quarter 3 Test, Form D

1. $\triangle BRG \sim \triangle NDK$ by SAS $\sim$ Theorem
2. $\triangle AYM \sim \triangle XQH$ by AA $\sim$ Postulate **3.** 12.8
4. 32.2 **5.** 13.5 **6.** D **7.** $4\sqrt{5}$ **8.** $\sin A = \frac{5}{13}; \cos A = \frac{12}{13};$
$\tan A = \frac{5}{12};$ **9.** $(10, 0)$ **10.** G **11.** 112 in.^{2} **12.** A
13. $5\sqrt{7}$ **14.** $x = 9, y = 15$ **15.** $y = 14$ **16.** $X'(4, 6),$

$Y'(5, 10), Z'(8, 7)$ **17.** $X'(2, -1), Y'(3, -5), Z'(6, -2)$
18. $X'(-2, -1), Y'(-3, -5), Z'(-6, -2)$ **19.** $6\sqrt{3}$
20. 88 ft **21.** 12 in. **22.** J

Quarter 3 Test, Form E

1. $\triangle WLB \sim \triangle HER$ by AA $\sim$ Postulate
2. $\triangle CMJ \sim \triangle FKP$ by SAS $\sim$ Theorem **3.** 24 **4.** 12.2
5. 63.0 **6.** C **7.** $6\sqrt{3}$ **8.** $\sin A = \frac{15}{17}; \cos A = \frac{8}{17}; \tan A = \frac{15}{8};$
9. $(-6, 9)$ **10.** J **11.** 588 in.^{2} **12.** A **13.** $8\sqrt{10}$
14. $x = 3, y = 25$ **15.** $x = 10$ **16.** $A'(0, 1), B'(-3, 7),$
$C'(-4, 2)$ **17.** $A'(4, -2), B'(7, 4), C'(8, -1)$ **18.** $A'(-1, 0),$
$B'(-7, 3), C'(-2, 4)$ **19.** $9\sqrt{3}$ **20.** 124 ft **21.** 3 in. **22.** F

Quarter 4 Test, Form D

1. 904.8 in.^{2} **2.** $4 : 7, 16 : 49$ **3.** 90 **4.** 75 **5.** B **6.** 96 cm^2
7. 8 **8.** 245.0 ft^2 **9.** 40 cm^2 **10.** 5 **11.** 9
12. 104 **13.** 90 **14.** 128 cm^2 **15.** 184 in.^{2} **16.** 180 cm^2
17. 201.1 ft^2 **18.** 133 **19.** 180 **20.** 192.5 in.^{2} **21.** 150.80 m^2
22. 188.5 cm^2

Quarter 4 Test, Form E

1. 1436.8 cm^3 **2.** $3 : 8, 9 : 64$ **3.** 65 **4.** 140 **5.** B **6.** 255 in.^{2}
7. 16 **8.** 326.7 in.^{2} **9.** 95 m^2 **10.** 10 **11.** 15
12. 90 **13.** 87 **14.** 125 cm^3 **15.** 804.2 m^2 **16.** 483.8 in.^{2}
17. 262 ft^2 **18.** 59 **19.** 239 **20.** 173.8 in.^{2} **21.** 94.25 cm^2
22. 55.0 in.^{2}

Answers (continued)

Mid-Course Test, Form D

1. $-9, -11$ **2.** 11 **3.** 16 **4.** $\angle T, \angle R, \angle S$ **5.** D **6.** 14
7. G **8.** 45 **9.** $C \approx 100.5$ in., $A \approx 804.2$ in.^{2} **10.** 10
11. $m\angle 1 = 38, m\angle 2 = 52$ **12.** SAS **13.** HL **14.** not
possible **15.** SSS **16.** AAS **17.** ASA **18.** 19 **19.** A
20. G **21.** $m\angle 1 = 105, m\angle 2 = 75, m\angle 3 = 105, m\angle 4 = 75$
22. parallelogram, rectangle, rhombus, square **23.** B
24. Hypothesis: a transversal intersects two parallel lines;
conclusion: alternate interior angles are congruent. **25.** J
26. A **27.** 166
28.

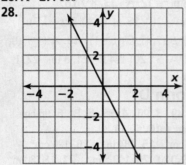

29.

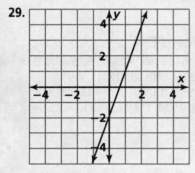

30. 42 **31.** (1, 2) **32.** 120 cm **33.** 13 **34.** G **35.** 24
36. 95 **37.** 157 **38.** $\overline{DX} \cong \overline{JX}$ **39.** $m\angle 1 = 40,$
$m\angle 2 = 95, m\angle 3 = 45$ **40.** $m\angle 1 = 54, m\angle 2 = 63$

Mid-Course Test, Form E

1. $-19, -23$ **2.** 13 **3.** 12 **4.** $\overline{RT}, \overline{RS}, \overline{TS}$ **5.** B **6.** 24
7. F **8.** 60 **9.** $C \approx 94.2$ in., $A \approx 706.9$ in.^{2} **10.** 13
11. $m\angle 1 = 47, m\angle 2 = 43$ **12.** AAS **13.** ASA **14.** SAS
15. not possible **16.** HL **17.** SSS **18.** 50 **19.** D **20.** J
21. $m\angle 1 = 80, m\angle 2 = 80, m\angle 3 = 100, m\angle 4 = 80$
22. square, rhombus **23.** A **24.** Hypothesis: a transversal
intersects two parallel lines; conclusion: corresponding angles
are congruent. **25.** H **26.** B **27.** 216

28.

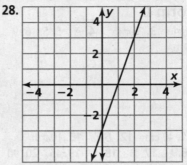

29.

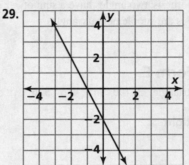

30. 52 **31.** (2, 1) **32.** 160 cm **33.** 23 **34.** J **35.** 47
36. 80 **37.** 67 **38.** $\overline{MZ} \cong \overline{TR}$ or $\overline{WZ} \cong \overline{WR}$
39. $m\angle 1 = 52, m\angle 2 = 30, m\angle 3 = 98$
40. $m\angle 1 = 59, m\angle 2 = 62$

Final Test, Form D

1. $x = 19, y = 135$ **2.** D **3.** hypothesis: if two sides of a
triangle are congruent; conclusion: the angles opposite those
sides are also congruent **4.** H **5.** A **6.** 62 **7.** 74 **8.** 91
9. G **10.** B **11.** C **12.** A **13.** D **14.** $A \approx 380.1$ in.^{2},
$C \approx 69.1$ in. **15.** $(-3, -4)$ **16.** $y = -x + 1$ **17.** AAS
Theorem **18.** ASA Postulate **19.** not possible **20.** SAS
Postulate **21.** HL Theorem **22.** $x = 8, y = 4\sqrt{3}$
23. F **24.** 200π cm^3 **25.** 40 **26.** B **27.** 90 **28.** 100 m^2
29. 11 ft **30.** 17 **31.** H **32.** 28 **33.** 71 **34.** 180 **35.** acute
36. center: $(-4, 3)$; radius: 7 **37.** $AC \approx 41.3, CD \approx 33.4$
38. 288 square units **39.** 8 **40.** 43.30 cm^2

Final Test, Form E

1. $x = 18, y = 147$ **2.** D **3.** hypothesis: if a point is on the
perpendicular bisector of a segment; conclusion: it is
equidistant from the endpoints of the segment **4.** J
5. A **6.** 150 **7.** 78 **8.** 76 **9.** G **10.** A **11.** D **12.** C
13. B **14.** $A \approx 907.9$ m^2, $C \approx 106.8$ m **15.** $(6, -2)$
16. $y = -x - 8$ **17.** SAS Postulate **18.** not possible
19. SSS Postulate **20.** HL Theorem **21.** AAS Theorem
22. $x = 12, y = 6\sqrt{3}$ **23.** F **24.** 540π ft^3 **25.** 8 **26.** D
27. 180 **28.** 128 cm^2 **29.** 14 ft **30.** 25 **31.** G **32.** 66
33. 68 **34.** 174 **35.** obtuse **36.** center: $(-6, 5)$; radius: 8
37. $MW \approx 43.5, MX \approx 34.3$ **38.** 80 **39.** 15 **40.** 173.21 in.^{2}

Informal Geometry Lesson Plans and Assessments